Willow's Story

The cases I reveal in my books are all based on true experiences, but I have changed names and some details to protect their identities as they go on to build new lives and families of their own.

THROWN AWAY **CHILDREN**

Willow's Story

Louise Allen

with Theresa McEvoy

MIRROR BOOKS

MIRROR BOOKS

1

Published in Great Britain and Ireland in 2024 by
Mirror Books, a Reach PLC business,
5 St Paul's Square, Liverpool, L3 9SJ.

www.mirrorbooks.co.uk
@TheMirrorBooks

Print ISBN 9781915306845
eBook ISBN 9781915306852

Design and production by Mirror Books.

Printed and bound in Great Britain by
CPI Group (UK) Ltd, Croydon, CR0 4YY

Cover image: Adobe Stock
(Posed by model)

This book was printed using
FSC approved materials.

To all the children and adults who have faced adversity in their childhoods — it does not define us!

Contents

Foreword   3

Chapter One   7
Chapter Two   16
Chapter Three   29
Chapter Four   39
Chapter Five   46
Chapter Six   49
Chapter Seven   55
Chapter Eight   66
Chapter Nine   72
Chapter Ten   83
Chapter Eleven   86
Chapter Twelve   95
Chapter Thirteen   103
Chapter Fourteen   110
Chapter Fifteen   125
Chapter Sixteen   135
Chapter Seventeen   141
Chapter Eighteen   147
Chapter Nineteen   156
Chapter Twenty   167
Chapter Twenty-One   173

Chapter Twenty-Two	184
Chapter Twenty-Three	196
Chapter Twenty-Four	215
Chapter Twenty-Five	220
Chapter Twenty-Six	233
Chapter Twenty-Seven	253
Chapter Twenty-Eight	261
Chapter Twenty-Nine	268
Chapter Thirty	274
Chapter Thirty-One	288
Epilogue	291
Afterword	300
Acknowledgements	304
Help and Information	306

Foreword

Willow is the tenth child I have written about in the *Thrown Away Children* series.

I have fostered more than 30 children in my years as a foster carer, if you include those who have come to me for short periods of respite care. Of course, it is generally only the children with the most dramatic or disturbing stories who make it into these pages. But, since I first began writing them, readers' responses have changed. Fewer people than they once did ask me questions like, "did that *really* happen?" or "it can't be *that* bad, surely?".

It seems that there is far greater awareness about the plight of children in care than there was even just five years ago. It's common knowledge now that the 'system' is broken. I no longer feel intimidated when I tell the truth.

I used to.

I used to worry about whether I should share some of it in writing. I used to go home and panic after a meeting where I'd dared to raise an issue that I felt strongly about. I used to think that it was my own, inner traumatised child popping up. But not anymore; not since I have worked with so many other foster carers, across the country and beyond, who all feel the same way.

Sometimes the reality is even worse than I am able to write about. And, with the guidance of my editor and the publishers, we decide to leave bits out, or at least to tell the stories with the most favourable endings. The reality of the dark side of so many children's lives as they are lived within the care system does not make for great reading. Sadly, truly 'happy' endings are few and far between.

Chapter One

Jason

'Well? What is the value of x here? Who can tell me?'

Bradshaw's words hang in the air like daggers waiting to fall.

'I'm waiting.'

Jason casts his eyes down towards the floor, willing it not to be him that gets picked on. Next to him, Kevin has his head down, eyes firmly focused on the blank page of his exercise book. Jason risks turning his head towards the window, searching for escape, and still desperate not to catch Bradshaw's roving eye. For one marvellous moment he feels he might float right out through it, away from this constricting hell. But the latches remain mockingly shut, the air stifling.

Another student behind Jason clears his throat as though he might be about to give an answer. No such luck. The silence expands. The classroom is a sarcophagus. They could all die in here.

'Anyone?' Bradshaw asks again.

Jason can't even process the question. The diagram on the board shows something impossible to do with circumferences. He can't even work out what 'x' refers to, let alone what the answer is. Who cares? It's not as if he is going to pass a maths GCSE anyway.

As if reading his mind, Bradshaw states, with undisguised cruelty, 'Not much point in asking you, Jason Wicker, is there?'

Someone sniggers in the row behind and he hears the whisper of 'Thick Wick'. It's a nickname he hates.

The bell rings, saving them all. The sound is immediately followed by chairs scraping against the floor, signalling the start of the barging race to join the explosive fizz of students out into the corridors and towards the exit.

The teachers used to make you wait and stand behind the desks, but then some students missed their bus and now the bell for the end of the day is a free-for-all.

'Bradshaw's got it in for you.'

Jason shrugs.

'I thought that lesson was never gonna end,' Kevin says.

'Yeah, right.'

'And it was stifling in that room.'

But not as stifling as what lies ahead for Jason.

He lingers longer than he should do with Kevin at the row of shops on the way home. There's a laundrette, a chip shop, a 7-Eleven store, a small newsagent that still does jar sweets that you weigh out, a charity shop and a Chinese take-away. It's somewhere to hang around after school when you have nowhere else to be. The trouble is, Jason *does* have somewhere else to be.

'Cola cube?'

Jason shakes his head. He doesn't have any money for sweets himself, never does. So he won't take one from Kevin.

'No thanks, mate. You're alright.'

'Suit yourself. Last chance.'

Jason knows he can't put off going home much longer, but he also knows what awaits him there. These days he tries to delay it as long as possible. Does everything he can not to think about it.

Kevin holds the bag tantalisingly close.

'Ah, go on then. Just one.'

The sweet, sharp taste on his tongue is delicious. He makes it last as long as he can, until the cube has become a tiny pip in his mouth.

It isn't fair on his mum, he knows that better than anyone.

'I'd better be off.'

Jason slides off the wall and slings his bag over his shoulder.

Kevin shrugs. 'See you tomorrow.'

Jason has a sudden urge to tell Kevin what it's like. To share all the worries that are in his head. To say it all out loud. Tell his friend what he's really feeling. How shit it all is. The exhaustion and the resentment. And the hopelessness.

But then he realises he wouldn't know where to start. And how stupid it would sound. Because Kevin has a normal life with a normal family and lives in a normal house. And anyway, who talks about stuff like that? No one. Definitely not Thick Wick. So instead, he says, 'Yep, see you then.'

Home is a maisonette on the Broadside Estate. Housing association. Now that his mum can no longer use the stairs, he and Andrew get to have a room each to themselves. Jason, as the oldest, has moved into what was his mum's room, but Andrew sometimes climbs into the big bed with him. At eight years old he should have grown out of that by now, but everyone says that Andrew is 'simple' so Jason lets him.

He puts the key in the lock. No escaping now. He bends down to pick up the post. Something from *Reader's Digest* that suggests they've won something. That can go straight in the bin because this family doesn't win at anything. And the usual raft of brown envelopes. Jason can't read very well, but knows they're never good news.

'Hi, mum. It's only me. I'm home.'

There is no reply.

There's a photograph of the two boys in the hall: Jason and his brother. He stops to look at it for a moment. Funny how you can walk past something every single day but only really 'see' it sometimes. He and Andrew have different dads but you wouldn't know it. They have the strong, maternal family look of bright ash blonde hair and brown eyes. They are both smiling in the picture: big toothy grins on display.

Everyone in their family has big teeth. Kevin sometimes takes the mickey out of him for having gravestones for teeth.

The small hall leads into the lounge where his mum hasn't moved from the spot where he left her this morning. About three feet from her bed to her wheelchair. A life with a three foot radius.

It's dark in there, even though it's only mid-afternoon. She hasn't opened the curtains today. That's not a good sign. The telly is on. *Win, Lose or Draw*. Contestants are given a phrase that they have to draw on an easel. Their teammates have to guess what they're drawing, with money on offer for the quicker they get the answer. The telly is always on. She will have run through ITV's full daytime schedule.

To be fair, it probably beat doing sums and talking about circumferences.

'About time,' she calls. 'Where've you been?'

'Nowhere.'

She snorts. 'Liar. It doesn't take that long to walk back from that place.'

And what would you know about walking? Jason wants to shout, but though he doesn't learn well at school, this life has taught him that any kind of reaction is futile. It's months since she's taken more than a few steps. Years since she's walked anywhere properly. She sometimes gets out and about the estate on the mobility scooter, but it's a monstrous thing which makes him cringe. It's embarrassing. But, of course, he keeps his mouth shut about that, too.

Instead he ignores what she's said and goes into the kitchen. 'I'll start making dinner,' he says, turning the oven on to heat up.

'Right,' she says.

'Jacket potatoes tonight. I'll put them in, then I'll go and collect Andrew.'

'Good lad.'

He's got used to how she can flip from cruel to kind in a fraction of a second.

The primary school finishes slightly later than the secondary school, but that doesn't leave enough time for Jason to get there after his own school bell goes, so there is an arrangement that Andrew goes home with a friend until Jason can get there to pick him up.

'Empty that first, would you?'

The old-fashioned chamber pot stinks, but Jason is used to it. He carries it out in front of him, away from his body. He trudges up the stairs and flushes it all away. It's not her fault she can't get up to the toilet. They're on the waiting list for a bungalow.

They're on the waiting list for a lot of things.

The bathroom sink needs cleaning. Most of the time he doesn't notice. Today he sees that it's got all scummy around the taps and there are lumps of toothpaste stuck to the basin. Andrew is yet to get the hang of keeping it on the toothbrush. Mum never comes up here now, so it's anybody's guess when it was last properly cleaned. The stairs are filthy. They need hoovering. Every room, every space inside the maisonette is disgusting. But that's Jason's fault. There's only him to do it. He should do more. If he didn't waste time dragging his heels on the way home from school. But there is always more to do. And none of it makes any difference. It's a shithole whether he tries to clean it or not.

'Carry me,' is the first thing Andrew says when they get outside.

Andrew's legs don't work properly. He's got an illness. Jason can't always remember the name 'Duchenne muscular dystrophy', but it's written down on the hospital letter that stays propped up on the microwave. They are big, unpronounceable words which really mean that Andrew's legs are weak and so he doesn't like to walk very far.

The condition was diagnosed more than a year ago now and will only get worse over time. It's a rare genetic condition that will gradually destroy his brother's muscles entirely. Andrew will probably need a wheelchair like their mum by the time he's Jason's age.

Jason tries not to think about that.

And when he does think about it he decides that it will be alright because they'll have a cure by then. Doctors are clever. The disease also affects Andrew's heart so he has to keep having check-ups. Their mum uses the mobility scooter to make sure that he gets to those. They'd have the social workers on their backs if she didn't. His mum isn't great at parenting but she's good with the social workers. She never gets angry in front of them. She makes sure that she comes across as reasonable, especially since concerns were raised about physical abuse.

Concerns have never been raised about Jason, but Andrew has drawn attention. He had red marks across his back one time and one of his teachers reported it. Their mum never hit Jason, not any more, but she did get frustrated with Andrew sometimes when he couldn't walk, or do the things that other kids could.

Jason bends down so that he can give his brother a piggyback.

'Not all the way. Just the first bit. You're getting too big and heavy now.'

'I know, but my legs hurt.'

At home, Jason prepares the dinner, then washes up and clears the kitchen. There's probably some homework due to Bradshaw for maths, or one of the other subjects, but none of it makes any sense these days and he can copy off Kevin in the morning.

He sends Andrew to bed first, then watches some more television with his mother. The same routine, night after night. After *Coronation Street* he encourages her to get into bed. She's always tired by 9pm, and she's been known to fall asleep in the wheelchair and then that becomes his fault, too.

'Ow, you're hurting me,' she complains as he helps her from the wheelchair back to the bed.

'I'm not doing it on purpose.'

Sometimes he wonders why everything has to be so hard.

Before he climbs the stairs again, Jason reaches for the brown envelopes. One has the emblem of the electricity company on it. He doesn't bother opening that one. The exact figure they still owe doesn't mean much. They'll never pay it off. It's all on a key meter now. It costs more because they're paying off the debt but he doesn't have to think about a bill. He must remember to top the key up on his way home from school tomorrow so that they've got enough to last them the weekend. Another thing to add to the list in his head. Sometimes there are just too many things to think about.

The other letter looks like it's from the social. He should probably leave that for his mum to deal with tomorrow, it's too late to give it to her now she's gone to bed. But something makes him tear open the envelope. Jason's reading isn't too good, but he sees enough before his eyes start blurring with tears. It's about Andrew and 'foster care'. They're going to take Andrew away. He ignores the fact that Andrew is going to a home that specialises in children with disabilities. Instead he focuses on the idea that it's all his fault. He has failed to keep their little family together.

If only he'd done more. He *is* a lazy, good-for-nothing waste of space, just like his mum always said he was.

Chapter Two

Louise
Present Day

'Bye, darling. Have a lovely time. Try and get *some* sleep.'

'I will!'

She won't.

Lily is having a sleepover at her friend Ruby's house. She clambers out of the car clutching her duvet and pillow along with a beach bag full of clothes and treats. In the rush to get to Ruby, who is standing waiting with the front door open, Lily barely gives me a wave or a second glance. She is growing up so fast in so many ways.

It seems to me that girls grow-up much faster than boys. Even though Jackson is older than Lily, he still needs 'mummy' at times, whereas Lily already seems so independent. If either Jackson or Vincent stub a toe, the first word they instinctively yell is 'mum'. Likewise, if they can't be bothered to look for a clean hoodie, the first word is 'mum'.

Is it gender? Or is it that Lily is my long term foster child and Jackson and Vincent are my birth children and that's what makes the difference. Who knows? Perhaps a bit of both.

I can feel Lily moving away from me little by little, though. I feel it and I fear it, but I also find it exciting that she is inching her way to becoming a teenager. I try to stop comparing them, because 'comparison is the thief of joy'. If you wish to be unhappy in your life, just compare your life with that of the others around you, especially those who are much more successful than you or you think are more successful than you. I thought it was Mark Twain who said it, but a quick Google tells me that it is, in fact, attributed to Theodore Roosevelt. What did we do before that little personal research assistant was at our fingertips?

But the boys are also 'easier' to deal with right now. I have experienced some strange, at times uncomfortable and unsettling scenarios with Lily of late. Not her doing, but men out there, in the outside world, who seem to think she is growing up even faster and that she deserves no respect. It comes from all quarters: boys at school, men cat-calling and wolf-whistling as she walks home from school, unsolicited 'compliments' from strangers in the street. It's terrifying, and I also suspect that I don't know the half of it. Lily hates telling me about anything like that happening because she knows how cross I get about it.

I want to pursue the men and give them a piece of

my mind. As though it's a localised problem rather than a systemic one.

The other day Lily walked into town to get some bits from Poundstretcher for her school art project. On the way home, as she was walking along a side street just off the High Street, an old man shuffling along with the aid of a zimmer frame called her a prostitute. Then, a few minutes later, as she walked a little further, in a fluster and close to tears, she happened to go past a white van. Two young men were sitting in the front. One wound down the window, gestured to his crotch area, and asked her if she fancied 'a suck of his cock'. What did she do to invite either interaction? Nothing other than being young and female.

When she got home she was understandably upset. As was I. I remember all this when I was a teenager in the 80s. I feel like the world ought to have moved on by now. It's hideous and violent. An accepted level of violence levelled at vulnerable girls. You could be forgiven for thinking that 2017's #MeToo movement never happened. When that erupted, I really felt as though things might start to shift. Turns out to have been a momentary uprising and then things dropped back to the way they were before. Maybe worse than they were before.

Perhaps it was nothing more than an unfortunate coincidence of timing to have both comments aired within moments of one another. Still, it's had a knock-on effect. Lily's response at the time was not to get angry, but to reflect and question what she was wearing.

'Do I really look like a prostitute?' she asked me, incredulous.

Her outfit was the teenage uniform of loose, dark blue denim shorts over thick black tights teamed with black Dr. Martens boots. It was a chillyish day so she was also wearing a black hoodie underneath her denim jacket. Hardly Madame de Pompadour. Or Julia Roberts in *Pretty Woman* before she goes shopping to accompany Richard Gere. And it was daylight in a relatively conservative area, not the red light district in Amsterdam after dusk.

But her insecurity over the encounter means that she's checked her appearance differently before leaving the house ever since, and not for reasons of vanity.

Why is it acceptable for men to verbally abuse her like this in the street? Every woman I know has memories and experiences of this nasty bullying, and nothing ever seems to be done about it. The boys at school say even worse things, not just to Lily but to other girls too. For six months or so a group of boys have been swaggering around the corridors and outdoor areas calling out things like, 'Kill yourself!' and 'Fat bitch' to Lily and other girls in her year group. For no apparent reason. When I have complained to the school, which is often, they say, 'Can you give us the boys' names?'

Lily will not, because she's scared of what will happen if she names them directly.

Sometimes she doesn't want to go to school, and I can see why. One idiot governor, a woman herself, who should have known better, said, 'It's just banter. Maybe it's their way of letting her know that they like her. Perhaps she should be flattered.'

When I managed to get my wide-eyed, you-are-an-absolute-arse stare under control, the best I could manage in response was, 'That's rather messed up, don't you think?' I wish I'd taken it further now.

Just yesterday, she decided to walk to a friend's house. The friend lives on the other side of town. Rather than going anywhere near the High Street and centre of town, which would have been much quicker, she took the long way round, avoiding town completely. She didn't want to see those men again. I made her promise that she would let me know if she encountered any of them. If she had texted me, then she knows I would have flown out and given them what for. I'm not sure which is worse from Lily's point of view: experiencing the abuse itself or my potential reaction to it.

But yesterday was different. It was a lovely sunny day and this time she was in leggings and a hoodie and trainers. It was some time mid-morning. She had her headphones on and was quietly minding her own business as she walked through a residential street. As she described it to me, a man and a woman were walking towards her. The man was holding a German Shepherd dog on its lead. The man was just 'a generic bloke in hoodie and jeans' but the woman was 'quiet and downtrodden'. Lily was simply walking along the footpath by the cycle track when the man called out to her.

'You shouldn't be out on your own. It's too dangerous. Unless you've got a hammer in your backpack. Girls like you get raped, then wonder why.'

Perhaps his words were meant with the best of intentions. Perhaps he wasn't threatening her, merely warning her. And yet, as she related the story to me, it turned into another episode of me wanting to find this man and his 'quiet' wife, and let rip. Each 'little' interaction serves to make me more and more angry with these bloody men. Who the hell do they think they are? Because his comments were loaded and stupid as far as I'm concerned. It was mid-morning in a reasonably public place. Is everywhere now dangerous for teenage girls? At any time of day? Who is responsible for making it dangerous? Men like Hammer Man.

Rather than scaring the hell out of an already freaked-out girl, as though she is the problem, why not start telling men to behave better? It would've been helpful if the woman with Hammer Man had spoken out, but no doubt she was frightened of him. And, as for suggesting that Lily should have a hammer in her backpack, I have no words. What good would that do if she was attacked without warning?

All of which goes a long way to explaining why I'm dropping her at Ruby's door, even though it's a perfectly walkable distance from our house. Thank goodness she's going for a lovely, fun, safe sleepover, away from arseholes. I truly hope that she makes the most of the time with Ruby and doesn't spend it scrolling through her phone. I hope

21

she's able to get past being fed-up with the world and is able instead to relax and laugh about how stupid some men's thinking can be.

I pull away from the kerb and do a three-point-turn in the street, conscious that however much I want to protect Lily and encourage her not to take things too seriously, it's actually no laughing matter. I find myself constantly fixated with how we improve the safety of girls. What kind of world have we created where it's a problem just to be able to walk around?

My adoptive mother, Barbara, who had herself been regularly sexually abused as a child (not that I knew it until almost the end of her life) would always say, 'Bloody men, they should cut their balls off.' My younger self was horrified and thought it was a dreadful thing to say. Not to mention wondering about who the 'they' was who should be doing this ball-cutting. But, now that I have been through the trials and tribulations of bringing up girls myself, I think I have slowly leaned towards her thinking – and perhaps even considered volunteering for the role. Both my stepdaughters experienced abuse from men, a number of my female students reported it to me, and most of my female friends have been through iterations of abuse at some stage in their lives. Of course, it's the kind of thing I refrain from saying in front of my husband, Lloyd – or he'd get nervous. I'll keep the big sharp knife in the block for the time being. Lloyd and the boys are safe. At least for now!

While Lily is chilling on her sleepover, I'm going out to a restaurant. It is, perhaps, somewhat ironic in view of all the thoughts I've just shared, but I'm sharing my evening with four men: Lloyd, Jackson, Vincent and Danny. Danny has recently turned 18 and is about to embark on his first year of university. He's been staying with us until his parents get back from Gibraltar. He comes from a naval family. We've known them for years. So long, in fact, that I was a waitress in a wine bar in Southsea with Danny's mum back when she first met his dad. He was a midshipman then, though he's risen to the dizzy heights of a lieutenant rank these days. His mother works in marketing at a sixth form college. I lived the trials and tribulations of their courtship while we waitressed together, then we went to their wedding. We've stayed in touch ever since.

They split their time between the UK and Gibraltar and had a little property to sell before they moved back to England to live. Danny, by his own admission, a bit bored with the life on offer in Gibraltar, had asked not to go. He wanted to spend the summer relaxing and hanging out with us.

I was only too pleased to say yes. I was quite touched, given that he's that much older than Jackson and Vincent, both of whom idolise him. It has also been something of a relief not to have to worry about another child in the house. Danny has been simply a delight to have around. He went to a well-known boarding school, and has emerged as a polite, informed young man.

The property deal is more or less concluded and so his parents will be back to pick him up in a few days' time. I'm going to miss him very much. Lloyd loves his company too. Lloyd's family also had naval connections and, even though Lloyd chose to go to art school, I think he secretly wishes he had joined the RAF or the Navy. He likes the camaraderie.

We don't have enough room for Brenda and Garth to stay with us in the house, so I've booked a double room for them in a little boutique hotel, 10 minutes walk away. The plan is that they will come here for dinner, then the morning after drive Danny to university in Sheffield, where he's heading off to begin a business degree.

So this is our separate 'goodbye' evening for Danny, and we've certainly pushed the boat out. (I find myself relying on boat and ship references more when Danny and his family are around.)

I've booked a rather fancy restaurant. Not just fancy, but award-winning. It recently celebrated receiving a Michelin star. For our area, that's an unusual accolade. I had to book several weeks ago to ensure we'd get a table. It has turned into quite the occasion. We all get dressed up. This involves me spending ages trying to get my hair to go into a hair bun donut, then having a crisis because when I look in the mirror I don't see the elegant, arty do that I'd imagined and instead look as if I'm trying to work for Virgin Atlantic. Now that I'm conscious of looking older, I just can't do 'severe' hair. I once used to emulate the style of the mannequin-like models in Robert Palmer's *Addicted to Love* video: all slicked-back hair, thick eyeliner, triangles of blusher carving out cheekbones, sharply-defined bright red lips. Alas, it's not a style I can pull off these days. Any attempt in that direction is liable to go more Widow Twanky than sexy siren. I end up with a floppy bun with stray bits of hair pulled out to soften the look.

We head out for dinner and I make a point of asking them what they think about Lily's plethora of current unpleasant experiences.

At first they are outraged, and say that they can't believe it.

'No, actually, true. If I'm honest, I *can* believe it. I'm well aware of it,' Danny pauses. 'And I'm ashamed of it.'

The boys nod in full agreement.

'It's totally unacceptable,' Lloyd says, with a shake of the head.

I remind him of when we were much younger, first going out together, and at an art school party. 'I had to waggle my finger at you and your friends in a stern way because I overheard you say something sexist about my friend, Roberta.'

'I remember. And no, that wasn't the start of our relationship. I was terrified of you for months after that!'

'Good! We've all got a responsibility to "call it out" when we see it,' I say. 'Because I do. I hope I always have done. But the older I get, the easier it has become.'

'You're absolutely right, Louise. It's not okay to make

girls and women feel bad about themselves for no reason other than they are female. That stinks! But it isn't always that easy to do.'

The boys open up a bit. We talk about the fact that men who want to do the right thing by women also have to navigate the peer pressure from other men.

'Toxic masculinity has become hard wired,' I argue. 'But actually, it's the very strongest men who are able to think for themselves and shrug off anxieties around what other men may think if they object to sexism towards girls and women.'

As I listen to the conversation flow back and forth, I take back much of what I thought earlier. I am surrounded by wonderful men. There are indeed plenty of good ones around. We just need more of them. And these are important conversations to have.

In the morning, Lily texts me to ask if she can stay another night at Ruby's.

I say yes and her reply text comes back almost instantaneously.

Great. Can I have some more money on my card? We want to go to the cinema.

I transfer the money, hesitating only to smile. All is good. I'm pleased, not to mention relieved, that she is evidently feeling better. If they're planning a night out then her confidence is coming back.

I spend some of the day making sure that Danny has everything he needs for university. His dad transferred some money into our account so we could get the bits and bobs he'll need. Clothes and new sports kit are top of the list. I think they've used us as a bank because if it was left to Danny then all the money would go on sporting equipment. Danny is the kind of young man who will join many sports clubs. We have sorted out pots and pans, crockery and utensils, and also bought him an air fryer along with a cookbook to help him use it. He and Jackson have been going to the local gym over the summer and have become very health conscious. It's great, but it costs the earth in protein drinks, bars and powder. I'm sure athletes just used to eat pasta and meat. Still, I don't have the 'elite' body myself to pass this judgement convincingly.

The rest of the time is spent getting the house 'shipshape', ready for the arrival of Danny's parents, until I'm interrupted by a call on my mobile. No caller ID, which usually means school or social workers.

It's the latter. An *urgent* referral for a girl of 13 years.

'Why is it an urgent referral?'

'I can't say too much over the phone, but the reason it's urgent is because we're in a situation where an allegation has been made. So the girl needs a placement immediately.'

I think about it for a few seconds and make my apologies.

'Nope. We just can't, I'm afraid. It would be too much right now.'

Especially as Danny is soon to leave and we want his departure to be as smooth as possible. Plus, we're really looking forward to seeing his parents and spending some decent time catching up with them. Lloyd has been pouring over cookbooks in preparation for some long lunches and relaxing evenings. We've put ourselves out so much over the years of fostering that we've done: taking on siblings or twins when we had decided that we could take care of only one, or impinging on family holidays and plans. Not this time. I make sure that I don't even get as far as hearing a name.

'No.' My tone is definite. Not to be argued with. 'For once, it's a firm no from us this time. Our circumstances won't allow it. The timing is all wrong. We have other commitments at the moment.'

'Oh.' The voice on the other end of the line is despondent. But this lady's not for turning.

'Yes, so I'm very sorry. Best of luck finding someone. Bye.'

Chapter Three

Jason

There is a giant, Andrew-shaped hole in Jason's life. His world was already small, but it now contracts even further.

Trying to manage the house and the business of caring for his mother seem even lonelier and more pointless without his little brother. It had felt like another burden when he had to worry about getting him back from school and feeding him, but the truth is that Jason misses the little fella horribly. Andrew gave him a reason to come home, and a reason to be a role model: a good big brother. With Andrew gone, everything feels empty.

Kevin has been the closest thing that Jason has had to a mate, but mostly just because they've known each other since reception class in primary school. It isn't much of a friendship beyond the classroom and the school field. And even Kevin doesn't seem to want to have much to do with him these days. Jason doesn't blame him. For a while he speaks to no one. Walks to and from school are even more desolate than they used to be, so finding a distraction on the way is important. And now that he doesn't need to pick Andrew up after school there's no reason to rush home. He starts tagging along with a different group of boys. Boys that his mother would probably say were 'trouble' if she knew. But what does she care these days?

It starts with dares.

Easy ones at first. Take handfuls of sweets from the newsagents without being caught. Steal out-of-date beers from the back of the 7-Eleven. Shout out things at passing strangers.

He feels more stupid when they get him to run through the local pub in just his underpants. At some level he senses that they're probably laughing at him rather than with him. He seems to be the butt of so many of the jokes. But he doesn't have any other friends and it feels better to be here with this lot than back at home with his mum who just blames him for Andrew being gone. She's bitter and angry and more difficult to be around than ever. He puts food in front of her and makes sure that she's out of bed and moved into the wheelchair in the morning. He forces the curtains open even when she protests. What more can he do?

Life rolls on.

In August, the GCSE results come through. They're as disastrous as expected. His best score is an F in Design and Technology.

'As useless as a chocolate teapot then, all that schooling,' is his mother's unhelpful verdict. 'Might as well not have bothered with it.' She sighs. 'What are you going to do now?'

He doesn't have an answer for that question.

'I dunno. Work?'

'As what? You're not qualified for anything. Andrew was the brains in this family.'

It turns out the school is not as useless as a chocolate teapot, because the careers officer there helps Jason fill out the application for a basic plastering course at the local college. He doesn't know if that's what he wants to do, but he has to do *something*. It can't be any worse than school.

The course turns out to be better than school because he doesn't have to do any writing. Boarding out walls and ceilings, and taping joints and preparing surfaces ready for plastering is easy. You don't have to remember too much in order to mix the materials. Gypsum and water and sand in the right ratios. He's strong, so he can lug around sacks of plaster compound with ease. He's not so good at skimming and finishing, but the tutors tell him that will come with practice.

There are other lads like him on the course, and no one calls him Thick Wick. He struggles with all the administrative stuff, but thankfully there isn't too much of that. The course is almost all practical. You don't need to be able to read once you know all the ratios and get a 'feel' for the consistency of the plaster. His mum was right. All that schooling was a waste of time.

Various teachers at the school accused him of having 'learning difficulties' at times over the years, which sometimes got him let off homework, but he's never received an official diagnosis. Busy with the challenges of Andrew's diagnosis, his mum never pushed for any help for Jason. Too late for that now.

Because he's big for his age, it's easy for him to get served in the pub where they go after college hours, even though he isn't yet 18. His size makes him look older, plus coming in in spattered overalls and boots is more convincing than school uniform. This superpower makes him more popular than he's ever been before, and provides him with a ready group of drinking buddies, of which Duncan is the ringleader. Of course, none of them have any money themselves, so Jason uses his mum's income support money to buy rounds. It makes sense, because he's the one who can get served most easily. It doesn't occur to him to ask the others to chip in. It just always seems to be his round until the money's gone.

There are other little perks to being at college. Everyone smokes roll-ups and it's easy to add a little bit of weed to your fag. Makes the days pass more quickly. Not only that, but Jason discovers that getting stoned takes away some of the guilt he feels over neglecting his mum and not seeing his brother anymore. Or at least the dope makes him forget about that side of his life for a bit, stops him feeling anything much for a while.

On his way back from the pub one night he heads to

the Chinese with one of the lads. The plan is to pick up a takeaway and then go back to his house to eat it and smoke a spliff or two. With his mum guaranteed to be asleep way before closing time, they can go upstairs and stay up all night if they want to. As long as they don't make too much noise, she won't know much about it. Anyway, immobile as she is, there's not a lot she can do about it. It becomes a bit of a pattern. Most of the other boys are living at home with their parents, but they don't have a mother with mobility issues who can't intervene, like Jason does. His mum complains a bit, but she can hardly come upstairs and tell them to be quiet.

'They're taking advantage of you,' she says in the morning. 'And me. You're an easy bloody target.'

His home on the Broadside Estate soon becomes the place they all hang out. Jason converts Andrew's old bedroom into a kind of sitting room den, and finds a cheap TV in the Friday-Ad to go in there. Duncan kips there some nights when they get too wasted.

One night on the way back to Jason's, they go to the 7-Eleven store to get some cans of lager. It's about to close up for the night; the shutters are already down. For once, Duncan nips in for the beers while Jason waits outside, rolling a fag. There are a group of teenagers hanging around underneath the lamp post. One of them is a girl he vaguely recognises from a year or two below him at school. He makes an effort with the cigarette-rolling, knowing that he's being watched.

He gives her a nod, attempting to look cool. His casual, 'alright?' comes out as a gruff 'orrwite'.

When Duncan comes out with the cans, he looks the girls up and down. 'You're in there, mate,' he says, as they walk back to Jason's. 'Reckon she's got the hots for you.'

After that, Jason looks out for the girl. He sees her a few times again, hanging out around the supermarket. She always smiles and nods hello.

'What's your name, then?' Jason dares to ask her one night, even though her mates giggle when he does and Duncan digs him in the ribs.

The girl is called Elaine and she is finishing her GCSEs. Jason is impressed that she is on track to pass five of them.

'You must be right clever, then. I never got any. Well one, but it was an F. Brainy Laney, that's what you are.'

'But you got into college.'

'Doing a plastering course. Not much longer to go and then I'll be working. Do you want to come to the pub on Friday?'

He loses his nerve when she hesitates.

'With your mates then?' he panics.

Duncan whistles. 'A right one for the ladies, you are, Jason!'

After a second, Elaine nods. 'See you Friday.'

Elaine and her friends manage to get into the pub and order some drinks, though she can only be 15 years old at most. She was at least two years below him at school.

Brainy Laney sticks as a nickname. He doesn't remind her that it's quite the opposite of Thick Wick. He never wants to hear that name again.

'I want to go to university one day.'

'Blimey.'

Elaine's Portuguese parents work at the food factory up the road, packaging microwaveable ready meals. It's long hours and unfulfilling work and, Elaine tells Jason, she has already decided that, whatever happens, factory work is not the life for her.

Jason ignores Duncan calling him a 'cradle snatcher' and arranges to meet Elaine again.

'Don't know what she sees in you,' Duncan says. 'You great lump of a bloke. Must be because you're older.'

Perhaps there is a glamour to being older, and closer to being in the workplace. Whatever it is, Elaine seems to like Jason, who never had a proper girlfriend at school. Their friendship develops over several months in spite of Duncan's ribbing. Jason finds that he is going down the pub less, and by doing that manages to hang on to most of his money. Perhaps his mum was right. Perhaps Duncan was taking advantage of him.

Instead of the pub, that summer he and Laney go down to the woods when the weather's nice, and smoke a spliff and lark about. Or stay in his house for the evening, upstairs away from his mum, listening to music and having fun.

Brainy Laney does indeed get her five GCSEs and

begins to get ready for college. But by then something else has happened that neither of them planned on: Elaine is pregnant. Her parents are furious and want her to have an abortion so that she doesn't ruin her life and waste the education she's already got. They regard Jason as 'simple', telling her that he'll amount to nothing.

'She can't have an abortion,' Jason's mum says when Jason confides in her. 'That ain't right.'

'But she's got to go to college, Mum.'

'Then let her have the baby and we'll take care of it.' Though his grandfather had died more than a decade ago and Jason barely remembered him, he knew that he'd been a strict, church-going man. His mother had therefore grown up in a church family who did not believe in abortion.

It's not something that Jason has given much thought to before, but he realises that he can't deal with the thought of abortion either. Or fostering and adoption. It brings back all the memories of Andrew being taken away. That can't happen to another child. It's too cruel. But him and his mum taking care of the baby? It's a crazy idea.

Elaine doesn't think so. 'Why shouldn't a baby live with her Daddy?'

'How do you know it's going to be a 'him'? Jason asks.

'Just do.'

The arrangement is agreed informally between the families and Elaine defers college for a year to manage the pregnancy before making a fresh start. She doesn't want her fellow students to see her pregnant. But there is a part of her, a young, naive part, that fancies that she and Jason can play happy families. Maybe she won't leave the baby.

'We could get a place. Move in together. Make it nice.'

'But I wouldn't be able to leave mum,' Jason explains. 'She can't cope on her own. It's impossible. And she's going to help me look after the baby.'

Living in an upstairs room with an invalid in-law downstairs isn't exactly what Elaine imagines. Besides which, her strict parents are having none of it. At their insistence she takes a job at the microwave factory while Jason continues his plastering course at college. Jason goes to the pub with his 'friends' less and less, preferring instead to spend time with Elaine.

They both love the fantasy film *Willow* starring Val Kilmer and Warwick Davies and watch it over and over again in the final months. The Warwick Davies character is a farmer who discovers a baby girl prophesied to end the rule of an evil queen.

'That's a good name,' Jason says one night.

'What is?'

'Willow. Kind of magical.'

'For a baby? Isn't the baby called Elora though?'

'I like Willow better.'

'For a boy?'

Jason shrugs. 'Or a girl! It's ambidextrous.'

'Not ambidextrous, that's when you're right and left-handed.'

'Alright, Brainy Laney.'

Elaine is thoughtful for a moment. 'Saves us thinking of two names, I suppose.'

'But I thought you said it was going to be a boy anyway.'

'I dunno. I'm not sure now,' Elaine says, stroking her distended belly. 'Willow,' she whispers. 'Magical.'

Chapter Four

Louise

Perfectly happy with my decision not to take in another teenager right now, I carry on about my day. I head down to my studio where, instead of working on the art commission I should be thinking about, I email Rachel about some practical details for my charity, Spark Sisterhood. She's the new operations manager.

She used to be a primary teacher and worked as a SENCO (special educational needs coordinator) and then SEND (special educational needs and disability teacher). The acronyms change frequently in education, as in so many other sectors. I knew Rachel would be an asset after she made sure that an EHCP (Education and Health Care Plan) was finally completed for a 10-year-old-girl who had been in care all her life.

No one had bothered to do the child's EHCP and it needed to be done before she started secondary school. They're not easy. To be honest, I'm not sure how parents and guardians get them done without professional help. Anyway, after launching the charity last year, I'm delighted to have Rachel on board. We are finding that it is a big workload. Even bigger than I expected. A worthwhile one, but taking up plenty of my time.

Nevertheless, after the recent events for Lily, I am more determined than ever to do my bit to help improve the lives of girls leaving care, which is the aim of the organisation. I'm still incensed about what has happened to Lily. But I'm also just as focussed on helping all girls reach their full potential in a world where the odds are still stacked against them.

All girls should be able to live their lives free from this insane archaic tyranny of male bullying and ignorance. Why should they keep being humiliated, side-lined, ignored and exploited? It's a sad fact that girls leaving care are more vulnerable, hence the charity, but until enough men are able to display the right attitude towards girls, all girls are at risk. Society isn't going to change overnight. The current climate makes our job even harder and even more necessary.

The phone goes. It's Moira, our supervising social worker.

'You've heard about the referral for Willow?'

Ah, so that's her name. Willow. I was trying to avoid knowing that. Still, it doesn't change anything. 'I have indeed, and I'm not keen. Not only do we have too much going on right now with Danny and his family, but she might also bring trouble. I gather she's made an allegation against her current carers.'

We've had our fingers burnt in the past with a couple of children who made allegations against their carers. There's always the risk that they might do it again, to us. We've also been on the receiving end of ridiculous allegations ourselves. We looked after Grant a couple of years ago, a lad who, unknown to us, had made multiple false allegations against his teachers and all his carers. He had clearly twigged that he could do this and garner a great deal of attention, but hadn't really thought about the consequences for the people he was accusing. The referral didn't mention it and his social worker kept quiet.

He was one of those placements where they just wanted to park the child and run. Then the cycle kicks in and another set of foster carers go through the mill. Rather than Social Services departments admitting incompetence, it seems that they make each foster carer feel like it has only happened to them and somehow it's all their fault.

In Grant's case there was a 'Home Link' book that first put me on guard. A lengthy paragraph had been written by the SEND teacher explaining that Grant had accused a member of staff of hurting him. It was quite specific: he was dragged and punched. The book also noted that the alleged incident had in fact never taken place, which was enough to raise a bright red flag. I took photos of the relevant page of the Home Link book as a kind of security. I've been doing this long enough to have learnt that it doesn't hurt to take copies of things that might protect you. I think the system is so tangled up with defensive self-protectionism that the truth isn't always easy to see, or sometimes to say. So, predictably, when Grant made an allegation against Lloyd, we were told that we were going to be investigated. Knowing that almost exactly the same description was given about dragging and punching, instead of getting defensive, I simply said, 'Bring it on!'

At the same time, a fostering friend in my WhatsApp group recognised Grant's name and put me in touch with another carer who had been through hell and was subsequently deregistered because Grant had pursued the same allegation against her − of being dragged and punched. It nearly destroyed her marriage. She and her husband were more than happy to send me their account. When the social worker threatened that they 'might have to call the police', my reply was very calm.

'Don't worry, I'll do it myself. Right now.'

I picked the phone straight back up and spoke to the officer in child protection, inviting him to meet with us. He was just about to retire. It transpired that he already knew of Grant and his allegation antics. I showed him our evidence and the statement from the deregistered foster carers.

His wry comment was, 'I'm surprised that they have any foster carers left.'

But the whole experience had left its mark, so to receive

a call about a child who had already made an allegation was a big fat 'no'.

Moira interrupts me.

'Oh, but Louise, that's not how it was. It was the foster carers who made the allegation against Willow.'

That brings me up short. 'Now that's unusual, and interesting. Tell me more.'

Foster carers write regular reports and communicate any incidents to the child's social worker. We don't, usually, make 'allegations' because there's no need. I can't imagine ever doing that; it just feels extreme and unnecessary. Hence my assumption that it was the child making the allegation.

Moira can sense the chink of light that this information has let in. She knows I'm puzzled. Moira has been our supervising social worker for a couple of years now. It's a level of consistency that we haven't been used to, but it's important because it means that we have been able to develop a good relationship over time. I know that I can talk openly and honestly to her without the danger that she might take offence. She is also a rarity in that she does occasionally listen to what I have to say. She is more than capable of holding her own in a 'robust' conversation, which is refreshing. She does keep threatening to leave, but so far so good.

'Go on then,' I prompt. I'm intrigued in spite of my every effort to avoid getting involved. 'What could be so bad that an allegation was made by foster carers about a child?'

'I don't have all the details, so I don't know anything

more about the nature of the allegation – but take another look at the referral. She sounds like a lovely child. It should be in your inbox. Read it properly.'

I promise that I will, and that I'll get back to Moira by the end of the day.

Once off the phone, I do what Moira suggested and read through the referral properly. No details about the allegation, of course. I'm fascinated to find out what she has done. Willow has been raised by a father with 'learning issues'. It doesn't say what those are, but it's clear that her mother isn't on the scene. The referral simply states that her father, Jason, 'could not keep her safe'. Later on there is a reference to the fact that his parenting 'was not good enough'.

And whose is? I think to myself, with a wry smile. We just do the best we can.

I plough on with the other tasks I need to, but I keep thinking about it. About Willow. About what she could possibly have done to trigger an allegation.

I don't seek out Lloyd in his office, but when I hear him go to the kitchen I find a reason to be there too.

'There's a referral I'd like you to look at. Obviously we're not in a position to take anyone right now, but it's quite unusual.'

I've printed it off, ready.

He reads it and makes a half-laugh sound.

'Exactly,' I say, knowing that he, like me, is astounded by the idea that a carer would make allegations *against* a child.

It just would not happen; it's unthinkable; it doesn't go like that.

'The question is–'

'The question is, what really happened? What is it that they're trying to cover up?' I finish.

I think we both know in that split second that Willow is coming to stay.

Chapter Five

Jason

By the time Elaine nears the end of her final trimester, the novelty of playing at keeping house has already worn off.

She is keener than ever to renounce motherhood, go to college and get on with her life. The time she has spent working in the factory has served as inspiration to better herself. It is a wake-up call as much as the pregnancy itself. She doesn't want to be limited to that kind of job, that kind of life. She wants to do well at college and go and make a different kind of life.

Elaine's parents have been clear from the outset that they are not going to help raise the child. They have saved up and bought some items to help Jason start out but, as it was his decision to go through with having the baby, he will be the one responsible from now on. Elaine's life is not going to be ruined by what has happened to them. She will be able to make a fresh start as soon as the baby is born. They all agree that it will be better for Willow in the long run if Jason begins being the main carer straight away. That way Elaine will not get attached to the baby and change her mind.

Jason takes one look at the newborn Willow, wrapped up in a blanket and sleeping peacefully in her cot, and is smitten. He doesn't understand how anyone could leave such a defenceless little thing. Perhaps she is a blessed baby, just like the little princess in the film that he and Elaine loved.

Jason's mum has also been inspired to make some life decisions.

'This baby, Jason. It's a new chance. Things are going to change around here. I've not always been the best mother, but I'm going to be a good grandmother.'

While Elaine's pregnant belly grew steadily over nine months, his mother's frame shrunk. She has been working hard to lose weight with the help of a local weight-loss group. She has been 'slimmer of the week' several times and has managed to shift 75 pounds. She has taken up small amounts of exercise and become a little bit more mobile again – enough to push a pram around the park. She has had some help to decorate the house, and between them they've got the box room ready for baby Willow.

With her new lease of life, and Jason's commitment to fatherhood, the arrangement somehow manages to work.

Or at least it does for a couple of years, until Jason's mum's health begins to decline again. She has been a heavy smoker since her teenage years and, as well as having diabetes, she also has emphysema and chronic bronchitis.

Her weight creeps back up and she finds herself struggling to keep up with a lively toddler.

Jason continues to work as a plasterer's labourer, which brings in some money, but not enough to fund the extra help his mum really needs to be properly able to look after a young child.

Then, two days after Willow''s third birthday, his mum dies of a sudden heart attack. Jason has no one to turn to. He and Willow are on their own.

Chapter Six

Louise

It's Danny's last night, and his mum and dad will be here for dinner later. I'm factoring in a hangover. We will almost certainly both have significant 'overhangs' because that's what happens when you have dinner with old friends who are in the navy. Is it a sign of age to be 'planning' a hangover? I buy some of those sachets that rehydrate you. I learnt all the tricks when I was a party animal with a full-time job. Sometimes I miss those days!

Lily is away again, returning tomorrow from a short school residential trip. That, on the back of a fun sleepover, is helping lift her spirits after all that misogyny.

So, tomorrow promises to be insane. Vincent and Jackson have made it clear that they will deign to join us for dinner, but will be gone straight after the food to get back on with their gaming.

'I should probably join them,' Danny says, with a twinkle in his eye. Danny and his parents will leave after breakfast to drive to Sheffield. Then Willow and her social worker, Rupert, will be here some time after lunch. Apparently, it's a bit of a drive.

When I spoke to Rupert on the phone he sounded very enthusiastic. And young. But who doesn't sound young these days? There are probably more things that I should be doing to get ready for Willow's arrival, but there just feels like too many things going on. There is the usual pre-dinner chaos. I just can't seem to get the cook, Lloyd, in gear. The plan is a rich Mexican chilli with all the trimmings.

'Perhaps you should stop drinking the wine?' I suggest, when nothing seems to be progressing in the kitchen.

All that does is elicit a raised eyebrow. 'If it was good enough for Keith Floyd...'

Meanwhile, I have the ingredients for Daiquiri cocktails. Two parts white rum, one part lime juice and a dash of sugar syrup. Absolutely delicious and the cocktail we all used to drink BC: Before Children.

Lloyd is chopping things and has several pans on the go. He's used 10 avocados to make the guacamole. The little speaker on the shelf is blasting out Talking Heads but I break off, momentarily, from my loud singing.

'Ten avocados? Seriously? You do know that from an environmental perspective this is now *a bad thing.*'

'They're good for you, no?'

'They might be, but more avocado plantations to meet demand has led to the clearing of forests, increased carbon in the atmosphere, soil erosion–' I say, in my best *Radio 4* voice.

'I can't hear you,' he jokes, miming putting his fingers in his ears. 'I wonder if the millennials are still having them crushed on their toast along with their latte-matte-natte coffees in that case.'

Life is what you make it and it all feels great.

The boys keep coming into the kitchen, making rude faces to divert attention, then stealing food before running off.

I love it!

These are the best times for me. Danny's mum is a vegetarian so I have made butternut chilli as an alternative to Lloyd's meaty one.

The evening passes far too quickly. It is wonderful to see Danny's parents again. They are such good fun, and so kind. We eat too much and drink too much and dance around the kitchen, laughing our heads off. It's so easy to slip into old ways with certain friends.

After they eventually wobble off to their hotel up the road, the boys ruthlessly mock us for our behaviour. For some reason (very possibly daiquiri-related), I think it is hilariously funny to chase them around the house wearing a sombrero while shaking Vincent's old castanets.

I make a decent start on clearing away the mess before I go to bed, though I'm flying solo. Lloyd was in bed as soon as we said goodbye. He loves to party but has no stamina.

Danny, having packed all his stuff last night, has put it by the front door ready for the morning. The sight of his bags makes me a bit sad as I go upstairs. It's been a wonderful evening.

I'm also up before Lloyd in the morning. I'm busy emptying the last few things into the dishwasher and making a much-needed coffee when Danny comes into the kitchen.

'I just wanted to say thank you, Louise. I've had the best time here this summer.'

My heart zings. I give this beautiful young man a big hug and try not to cry. He is truly delightful and I think he has been such a good influence on the boys. I'm fairly certain Lily has a bit of a crush on him but, with all the misogynistic experiences she's been subjected to of late, she's a bit wary of males in general.

I make a big fry up for whoever wants it. Me, primarily, but the boys travel down once they smell the bacon. They have 20 minutes until they head off to school and it's nice for them to spend a little bit of time with Danny.

'You'll all miss each other, won't you, now that you won't see each other for a while,' I observe. They look a bit puzzled. Then Jackson fixes me with a stare that leaves me under no illusion that I'm anything but an idiot and says, 'We're all gaming later.'

'Of course you are.' I shake my head. The virtual world and the real world are much closer for them.

Jackson and Vincent head off to school. Lily will return

from the residential later on this morning. Lloyd is still tucking in to a huge fry up when Danny's parents, having had breakfast at the hotel, arrive. There is more coffee, more laughing, and an urgent need for two paracetamol. There is no hurry. It will be better to leave mid-morning once the rush hour traffic has cleared and the roads are freer for the drive up north.

At the point at which Danny's bags are being stacked in the back of his dad's Range Rover, I feel the tears coming. I use my hangover as the excuse for being over-emotional. Lloyd stands in the doorway and I'm leaning into the passenger seat saying final goodbyes when all of a sudden a pale blue Fiat 500 swings in front of the Range Rover.

I probably look confused, because I am. It's not a car I recognise. At the same time, on the other side of the road, Ruby's mum appears in her car with two girls in the back, one being Lily. I wave. They're earlier than they said they'd be.

Danny's dad laughs. 'Good luck.'

He waits for the blue Fiat to creep back a bit so he can pull out, but it doesn't. Instead, out comes a lean-looking girl with short, sensible hair. She is dressed most peculiarly. A bit like an old-fashioned boy scout in long shorts and a teal-green shirt, buttoned right up to the neck. She is only missing the necker and woggle. It must be Willow. Beside her is a man who I assume must be Rupert. He is young, tanned and sports a dyed blonde quiff. He's wearing a long

53

puffer coat in a showy golden olive colour over blue jeans and immaculately white trainers. He begins waving at us cheerfully.

Lily, meanwhile, still on the other side of the road, starts shouting, 'the dogs, the dogs!'

Douglas and Dotty, our crazy jackahuahuas, have escaped into the road to join in with the hellos and goodbyes. There are cars everywhere, beeping, and drivers shouting.

Danny winds down the back passenger window and calls out, 'Do you want to come with us?' and laughs.

Willow, seeing the chaos around her and reading the situation, grabs hold of Dotty.

Lily chases after Douglas and scoops him up into her arms. 'Hi,' she says, shyly. I haven't had a chance to let Lily know that Willow was coming today and anyway, I thought she would be here later, after lunch. Nothing is ready. We all wave to Danny as they drive off laughing. I welcome everyone in.

Oh, my head hurts!

I have definitely not brought my A game to today's proceedings.

Chapter Seven

Louise

To say that I'm less than excited about Willow and Rupert being here three hours ahead of their appointed time is an understatement. I have nothing ready and the house smells of fry-up. The kitchen looks as if a fight between a pack of racoons has taken place across all the surfaces. I feel very much on the back foot and the paracetamol are not doing their job yet: my head still throbs.

There is another knock at the door. Of course there is.

Lily is still in the hallway manoeuvring her sleeping bag from the overnight residential, so she is the one to open the door. It's *another* social worker. Lily shows her into the kitchen where she finds all of us jostling for seats and me scraping bacon rind from greasy plates and piling up cups. I stash it all in the sink for now, then turn around mustering my best Julie Andrews smile. 'Now, would anyone like a drink?'

The second social worker is called Kirsty and at a guess she is probably my age, though looks much older – but that's what happens when you wear beige and have a 'helmet' bob cut. I decide instantly that I don't like her. She introduces herself as Rupert's line manager and does not look very approachable, though she is friendly with the dogs, so she's not all bad.

I'm not sure yet what to make of Willow. She's a timid little thing, and she has stepped into chaos, so I can't blame her for looking slightly bewildered by it all. She reminds me of something, dressed in her weird attire. I take a moment to work out what it is. It comes to me in a sudden rush: *Cabaret* with Liza Minnelli, my most favourite film in the world. There is a scene where the Hitler Youth sing *Tomorrow Belongs to Me*. I'm not suggesting that Willow herself looks like she might be a Nazi, but her outfit is bizarrely suggestive of the uniform.

She has soft wavy hair, cut into a bowl. It's the sort of haircut that visiting aunties delivered in the 1970s. Everything about her looks old-fashioned, from head to – good grief, are those plimsolls on her feet? Quite the contrast with Rupert, who is still wearing his golden olive puffer coat. He looks more like a member of the production team for *Love Island* than a children's social worker. When he smiles I see his whiter-than-white pearls of teeth. Wow. He's like a toothpaste advert.

I had my teeth whitened once. In some woman's house, whose advert I'd seen in the paper and then heard about from acquaintances. In the back of her garden she had two posh sheds set up so that the two 'teeth women' could get through as many people as possible in a kind of production line. They wore white overalls and I'm not entirely sure about the science, but one shone a blue light into my mouth for half an hour. I left with a migraine and a free gift of branded travel-size toothpaste. That cost me £100 and, although my teeth were dazzling white initially, after a few days they went back to their normal colour. I have often wondered if she has since been closed down. I certainly stopped seeing the advertisements. Older, wiser, I'm not sure if I would do it again. Afterwards, it seemed as if my teeth were too white – as are Rupert's right now. And a few days later it was all for nothing anyway.

What a funny group of people appear to have assembled in my kitchen.

Lloyd excuses himself to take a call with a client that he deliberately arranged for now because he thought, like me, that Rupert and Willow would be here early afternoon and not this morning. I step nonchalantly over the pile of sheets and bedding that Danny kindly brought down after stripping his bed, although they now appear to have taken on epic proportions in the crowded room. Doug settles himself down to sleep on top of the pile. I think he misses Danny already. Lily chooses this moment to empty out her pack of washing onto the floor too.

So here I am: thumping headache, zero preparation, a messy house, a mountain of laundry. Terrific.

Kirsty smiles. 'A woman's work is never done, Louise!'

Those sorts of comments rile me because I resent the expectation that the toil is women's work. Fostering is one of the most misogynistic industries there is because our home is our workplace. The domestic setting seems to highlight the way people treat women.

Not in my house!

I need to get through this as quickly as possible and with a degree of dignity, which frankly I will have achieved if I manage to make it through the entire meeting without being sick. The headache is being joined by nausea. What I really need is a little lie down. Or at the very least, some fresh air. I open the window, wishing that I could just float away through it.

I notice Willow looking around the bomb site of a kitchen. I decide not to apologise since they are the ones who arrived early. Instead, I say, 'You've caught us on the hop. We weren't expecting you until after lunch.'

Having delivered her laundry, Lily remains hovering. She is hungry and no doubt tired after her double sleepover and trip. Her teenage brain is focused on food, not people. She can't wait any longer. She has no doubt been thinking about food all the way home. I know that girl well.

Never mind the audience, she opens the fridge door anyway and starts rummaging away.

'Don't mind me,' she says, balancing a pile of yoghurts, a carton of blueberries and some other bits from the fridge and cupboards in an awkward pile. 'Pretend I'm not here,' she smiles as she heads back in the direction of her room. I know that she hasn't got a spoon, but decide not to question it. Rupert takes over and starts pulling a load of paperwork from out of his messenger bag.

'Let's get started, shall we?'

Poor Willow. What a process. I smile at her as reassuringly as I can. She seems very wary and looks totally harmless. We have had some characters here over the years, and I've come to expect the unexpected, but she really doesn't look the type to cause trouble. What on earth did she do that warranted an allegation?

We trawl through the various documents that Rupert spreads out in front of him. I have learnt to nail the 'delegated authority' paperwork first. This is the boring but important part of the process that enables foster carers to make common sense, everyday decisions about the children in their care. Things like allowing them to go to friends' houses for sleepovers, signing consent forms for school trips and arranging haircuts. Foster carers technically don't have parental responsibility for a fostered child, but the holders of parental responsibility can delegate authority to foster carers to undertake those common sense tasks and decisions on their behalf.

I sign away. I certainly think a trip to the hairdresser is in order to bring Willow's hair up to date. She is too old to be wearing a set of white kitten hair clips, pulling her hair away so bluntly, or to have such a sensible but unflattering haircut. It could look kitschy-cool on a young, media type, but not on this mousy 13-year-old. She honestly looks as if she's been transported from a 1950s children's annual and is about to embark on a jolly adventure with her chums.

Lloyd's business call with a client ends and he rejoins us in the kitchen. I know he keeps headache tablets in his desk drawer so is probably suffering less pain than me. He just looks a bit tired. He knows me well enough to know that I am not doing well.

I caught a glimpse of myself in the hall mirror and my usually olive complexion is the colour of putty. I'm not presenting my best self here. I feel sick and I just want these people to go. Looking at Willow, so does she. But I do notice that she is wary of Lloyd. She watches him carefully. That tells me a lot, and I will be carefully observing. I make a mental note to tell Lloyd, when this lot eventually go, to keep his distance until Willow learns some trust.

More forms. More chat. I'm finding it hard to concentrate and engage. Eventually the beginnings of chair shuffling signal that the round of goodbyes will begin. I close the door and head back into the kitchen to find Willow sitting on the chair bent over the dogs who are only too happy to soak up the attention. I let out a big, 'Phew.'

Willow looks up expectantly.

'Blimey, that went on a bit, didn't it?'

She shrugs.

'So finally, I get a proper chance to say hello. Willow, it's lovely to meet you.'

She smiles, revealing a set of large teeth. I make another mental note, this one about arranging an appointment at the dentist. There are 5000 children in the area without a dentist, according to a local BBC report. Sometimes I can't believe the state of the local area, let alone the rest of the world. Thankfully, we still belong to the only remaining NHS dentist in town.

'Are you hungry? How about a sandwich?'

My blood sugar levels require something, even if hers don't. I fill a big glass full of water and gulp it down. I then go into the cupboard and take out a packet of paracetamol, push two out of the blister pack and knock them back.

'So, would you like cheese, ham, cheese and ham, jam, peanut butter, jam and peanut butter?'

She looks at me, one eyebrow raised. Amused? Or bewildered? It's hard to tell.

I continue, 'Cheese and jam? Ham and peanut butter?' I start laughing, and so does she. What a poppet she is, but those clothes will have to go.

I pull out some crisps from the multi-pack in the cupboard.

'Which flavour takes your fancy?'

She grins, exposing those wide teeth once more. 'Salt and vinegar, please.' What a polite child.

I hand her the packet. 'Excuse me for one moment,

Willow. I'm just going to call Lily down to see if she would like some lunch now that the coast is clear.'

Lily appears a moment later. 'Hello, Willow. Welcome to the madhouse.' She's good at welcoming new arrivals, remembering herself what it's like to be one. She has showered while the social workers were here, and now has wet hair dangling in her face and dripping onto her grey hoodie which she is wearing over her pyjama bottoms.

'Are you off to bed?' I ask, indicating her bottom half.

'I'm tired,' she yawns.

'Okay, my little sweetness, after you've had some lunch, why don't you and Willow go and watch a film in the sitting room? I'll bring in some sweets and popcorn.'

Willow looks amazed at the suggestion, the raised eyebrow making another appearance, but says nothing. I bring out the dips from the fridge for the girls to dip their crisps in.

'So, Lily, how have the last few days been?'

She munches on crisps, and some energy returns to her. 'It was awesome.'

Despite my somewhat-improved headache, I decide that I really fancy some ice cream. It must be the sugar that I'm craving.

I take three bowls from the rack and plonk them down on the table. Then I pull out two tubs of Kelly's ice cream from the freezer. A honeycomb crunch, and a clotted cream and raspberry ripple. Willow's eyes light up.

'A bit of one or a bit of both?'

'Both, please.'

'Good choice.' I take the metal scoop and run it under the hot tap before scooping out generous balls of ice cream.

I savour the cool flavour slipping down, and feel the sugar surging through my hangover, bringing me back to life. For a moment the only sound is the scraping of spoons against bowls.

When we're done, Willow follows Lily into the sitting room. I hover by the door to hear how this goes.

'Am I allowed to sit on the chairs?'

Lily says, 'Yeah, of course,' and then in that wonderful uninhibited way of children, asks her directly. 'Weren't you allowed to sit on the chairs in your other home?'

That whole sentence is good. Well done, Lily, I think. It is simultaneously welcoming and affirming for Willow.

'No. I had to sit on the floor on a cushion. My foster carers had the sofa and chairs.'

Lily is nonplussed, offering only an acknowledging 'Huh' in reply.

I leave them to it and go and chuck Douglas off Danny's bedding.'

He summons the best 'injured, self-pity, feel-sorry-for-me face' as he finds himself back on the floor. He makes a slow, huffy walk over to his official bed and gets in it with a sigh, throwing me another 'how could you?' look for good measure.

I retrieve the plates and cups from the sink and make a proper start on clearing up. After about 20 minutes I have managed to uncover surfaces once more and the kitchen looks much more like my kitchen again.

I pop my head around the sitting room door. Both girls are fine. Lily is lounging on one sofa and Willow is sitting bolt upright in the centre of the other, looking like an illustration for how to acquire good posture.

I grab the Henry and vacuum the floor of Willow's bedroom and the bathroom, and then give the hallway a quick going over. I wipe down all the surfaces and then head to my airing cupboard of love, inhaling the aroma of the many fancy bars of soap that are stuffed in amongst the bedding and towels. It always makes me feel settled and balanced. I pull out a simple set of stone-coloured bedding and a new white cotton sheet. I keep reed diffusers at the bottom which I buy when I see them in the sales. I select one called 'Herb Garden', deciding that it sounds lovely and fresh. I make Willow's bed and there we are, a nice clean room ready for our very special new arrival. You'd never know a teenage boy had been here for weeks. Danny, the sweet boy, has opened the window so that the room is already aired and feels fresh. I hope some of his thoughtfulness has rubbed off on Vincent and Jackson, though I know the reality is that they do remember their manners when they go elsewhere. It's only at home I get the dubious privilege of their relaxed attitudes.

I'm just putting the vacuum cleaner away when, with impeccable timing, Lloyd comes to find me, safe now that the work is done. 'How are you feeling?' he asks.

'Okay, I suppose. I'm alive.'

He leans in and whispers, 'What do you think?'

'The hair and clothes must go. She'll be stared at and teased.'

He nods. 'Exactly what I thought.' Then, with a perplexed frown, 'A bit Hitler Youth.'

Chapter Eight

Jason

It's tough to cope with his mother gone. There is the immense weight of grief, but also the fact that it was his mum who took care of all the life admin involved in running a household. With her gone, the brown envelopes pile up. Jason doesn't know how to deal with all the complex things that have to happen in the aftermath of death. And there is no one else to ask. His priority, though, is always Willow. Years of cooking and caring for his mum have prepared him well for the relentless pressures of looking after a young child. But Jason's learning difficulties mean that even something as simple as registering Willow for primary school is beyond him.

One day a solution presents itself. On his way out of the 7-Eleven, a kindly-looking lady thrusts a leaflet into his hand. It just says 'Smile' on the front, with a picture of a smiley face. He doesn't feel like smiling but the leaflet says he should smile because God loves him.

'What a bonny little girl,' the lady says, smiling at Willow.

She is a member of a local church. It turns out that there are people connected with the church who will help. They are good people, kind people. It really feels as if he has been blessed. They visit him at home and show him how he can access additional financial support. They donate clothes for Willow. Some of the ladies bake cakes and treats. He's used to cooking; he grew up making the meals for them all while taking care of his mother, but it's nice to be looked after for a change.

It isn't just about prayer, there's all sorts of activities up at the church hall. He can get help with everything. They even help him to fill out the forms that he needs to in order to get Willow into the school for the following September. Not only that, it is like being given an instant circle of friends, and is somewhere to go where people are kind. They begin to attend church every Sunday and it all brings great comfort to Jason who has felt lost, sad and unable to cope since his mum died.

Some other men from the church knock on the door and offer more regular help with prayer. It requires space at home. Willow is moved from her little bedroom into sleeping on a mattress on the hall floor while Jason and the men convert her room into a prayer room. It's a good arrangement.

When Willow starts reception class she thrives. She is such a clever little thing. She definitely gets her brains from her mum and not from Jason. Jason thinks about Elaine from time to time, wonders what Brainy Laney is up to, hopes that she managed to get to university like she wanted to. She was clever enough. Not like him. He doesn't have any way of contacting her though, and her instructions about him being totally responsible for bringing up their child were very clear. He still carries the weight of Andrew's loss and remains determined that another child will not be taken away from him.

Although Willow is very bright, it's soon noted by her teacher that something is wrong. Willow has some strange ways and says some odd things to her peers. When the local vicar comes in to talk to the children about the change of the seasons, he drops a samara fruit, also known as helicopter seed, by holding it up and letting it go. Willow becomes inexplicably upset. Her tears are compounded when the vicar says a prayer at the end of the assembly.

'Lord, I offer you this new day. I offer you everything that will happen. I offer you the routines and the challenges of the day ahead. Help me to keep listening to you, to do what you inspire in me and to shoulder the crosses that wait for me on this day's journey into learning, friendship and love with you.'

The children join in, with a chorus of 'AMEN', but Willow sobs and seems scared.

Her teacher takes Willow aside to check that she is okay.

'The high priest said that me and daddy are not praying hard enough and that if I am going to be put on the fire I must pray harder.'

'Put on the *fire*?'

Willow's words instantly raise the alarm at the school.

A meeting is set-up with children's social services, Jason and the school. Unable to read the missives that are arriving, Jason shows the men from the church and the prayer room is quickly dismantled. Jason is briefed by the members of this church offshoot about how to handle the meeting and what to say in answer to certain questions. He remembers how good his mum was at this sort of thing and takes their advice.

There are two social workers present at the meeting which, considering the lack of human and financial resources in the sector, seems quite extravagant. Jason had help getting ready and arrives at the meeting looking smarter than he has done for months. Gone are the ripped, plastering overalls. Instead, he has his hair neatly combed and is wearing a clean pale blue shirt and slacks. He adds his cleanest white trainers for a convincing presentation.

The social workers have spent half an hour with Willow just prior to the meeting to try to decide if there are any grounds for concern. Willow, like her father, has been well briefed by the church men, reinforced by her dad who has parroted what they say. Those men know their stuff. It's almost as if they know exactly what the social workers will ask. Jason and Willow are able to head off every question. Willow has been promised a scooter if she is a good girl and gets all the answers she has learned right. She has wanted a scooter for some time and is a fast learner.

During the meeting Jason performs very well. He is polite

and enthusiastic and keeps saying how much he appreciates their advice and support.

'Can you tell us what a normal day is like at home?'

Jason describes the cooking, cleaning and caring tasks that he performs. He talks about the way he used to care for his mum.

The social workers, having visited their home earlier in the day, are convinced that the care is good enough.

'The flat was clean and there was plenty of food in the fridge and cupboards,' one reports. 'Willow had a nice clean bedroom with lots of books to read and toys.'

Willow nods enthusiastically, and does not mention the fact that she had been sleeping on her mattress in the hallway until just a few days before.

Jason mentions the church group and how much help he is receiving from them.

'Willow seemed upset when the local vicar gave a prayer in assembly,' the teacher insists. 'Can you think of any reason why that might be?'

Jason responds very cleverly with his stories of Sunday school and how 'Willow knows lots of different prayers and enjoys them very much.' Perhaps the vicar just used different words to the ones that Willow is used to, he suggests. He also explains how Willow 'loves stories from the bible,' just as he had been briefed. He keeps saying that they have, 'a child friendly version with lots of lovely pictures'.

Willow nods enthusiastically once more, even though she

has actually only attended Sunday school once – last Sunday – on the suggestion and organisation of the men who made the prayer room.

Although he clearly has 'some learning difficulties,' Jason has an answer for everything. The meeting is a success. The social workers close the case and, after the heat has gone and Jason is no longer under scrutiny, Willow gets her scooter and the men once again take over Willow's bedroom as a 'prayer room'.

Chapter Nine

Louise

I'm still upstairs sorting Willow's room when the doorbell goes. I guess at this time in the afternoon it's probably a delivery. I pretend I haven't heard it and let Lloyd go and deal with it.

'Louise?' Lloyd calls up the stairs. 'It's Moira.'

I totally forgot she was coming, and she's here at the right time, unlike the others.

She looks at Willow's bags, still down in the hall, yet to make it up the stairs. Four bin bags. Never a good sign. It smacks of 'you're not wanted and you're not good enough'.

'They came early? Why didn't you tell me?'

To be honest, in the chaos and overhang, I haven't thought about Moira at all.

'I'm sorry. It all happened so fast. Cuppa?'

'Definitely.'

'Good, I'll put the kettle on.' While the kettle builds itself up into a frenzy as it approaches boiling, I ask if

Moira knows of Kirsty, the social worker who arrived with Rupert.

'Kirsty, you say? No, I don't think so. Definitely not,' Moira says, tucking into a biscuit.

I'm somewhat surprised. They are both lifers in Children's Social Care so it's extremely unlikely that their paths would *never* have crossed. Perhaps she isn't telling me the truth. I imagine that there must be a very strict code of conduct rule which prevents anything negative being said about a fellow social worker in front of a foster carer, parent or child. But amongst themselves, I reckon they must have the odd bitch-fest. They are stepping on each other's toes all the time. And, when the working conditions are poor, tensions rise.

So, for a while now, we have quietly been looking at moving away from the local authority. I have been to visit a number of independent fostering agencies (IFAs), some representatives of which have been to the house. So far, I have only managed to find one I like. Only one, from dozens, that straight away gave the impression of prioritising the children, actually caring about them as individuals, and treating the foster carers well. The rest seemed to be a lot of sales talk, and left us with a general feeling that we would be treated badly. One agency claimed to be a 'family run' agency. That didn't seem to be the case when I looked them up at Companies House, the executive agency sponsored by the government to register company information and make it available to the public. This particular IFA, who shall remain nameless, tried to sell us the idea that if we did loads of extra work, like telephone other carers to see if they need support, or drive carers and their children around, or run events, then we would have the opportunity to earn another – wait for it – £7 per week. I politely declined, of course. But the reality is that there have to be alternatives to the current model of provision.

Not least because our local authority has recently declared itself bankrupt. It's not the only one in the country, but it's still shocking. Though, thankfully, we had decided to leave long before that horrible announcement came. Whatever happens, it looks like Willow will be our last foster child through the mainstream system.

A friend of mine who was once an accountant for another local authority and now works in the charity sector, told me that the commissioning of private fostering agencies is actually cheaper than when local authorities use their own in-house fostering services. I am an artist first and, to my little non-financial brain, this business side of things makes little sense.

Foster carers are paid peanuts. That is no secret, and it isn't the first time I have drawn attention to the fact. The allowances seem much healthier in the private sector. With the current cost of living crisis, it's not rocket science to deduce that so many foster carers have to work additional jobs to be able to afford to look after the foster children in their care. It's not a recipe for the best circumstances for the neediest children.

Moira changes the subject. 'Before we do anything else, I do need to tell you something.'

Oh no, here it comes. After we have accepted the referral and Willow is now ensconced in our home she is going to tell me that Willow attempted to murder her last foster carers.

I'm totally wrong.

Moira makes a gentle little cough to clear her throat and says, 'I will be leaving in two months' time.'

I am taken aback and not quite sure how to respond, or what words to say. It's fair to say that I do suffer from societal inappropriateness, borne of childhood trauma, which basically means I laugh at the wrong things. Or maybe I don't; maybe everyone else is serious about the wrong things. Who's to say? Either way, I laugh!

It is not the reaction that Moira expects. She gives me a peculiar look.

'I don't blame you,' I say, finding the words at last. She smiles at that, and shakes her head. I mean that the management that has led to a bankrupt local council is a good reason to switch to another authority. Social workers always claim that they can't be political, but they use that definition more widely than simply in reference to party politics. Of course they must not say anything negative about their employer, however much they might want to. In practical terms, Moira's employer, the local authority, is the same employer as mine, but as foster carers we do not have employment contracts or rights. This leaves me far freer to say what I want. But it isn't always well-received. If I am critical then I am accused of belonging to a minority of negative voices, because all the other foster carers in the world must be just so happy about the broken system.

'I'm leaving the sector altogether.'

'To do what?'

'Well, I've actually accepted a job with a company that organises weddings.'

'Wow Moira, that sounds like much more fun.'

'It's also better paid, better hours and the team is lovely.'

I genuinely could not be happier for her.

Moira then tells me that she is looking into which supervising social worker would best suit us.

This is when it gets slightly awkward. I say, 'Well, about the same time that you leave, we will also be moving on.'

She looks at me aghast.

I explain that, for over a year now, I have been researching and meeting different independent foster agencies. 'Mostly disappointing, but I'm confident that we have found one that looks like it will suit us better than the current system. It's that or retire from fostering, I'm afraid.'

Moira is stunned. 'Oh, Louise, is it something I have done?'

I try to reassure her that this would have happened anyway, and remind her that she's just announced that she's leaving too. In my emotional (hungover) state, something has been unleashed and I'm ready for an outburst.

'It's not you. It's the system. I'm tired of fighting for every little thing, let alone the big, important stuff. I need someone else to take that burden away from us so that we can get on with the business of looking after the children. It's become exhausting. The children deserve better than worn out foster carers.'

There is an uncomfortable pause before we both realise that, in spite of our simultaneous decisions to leave our local authority, we do need to get back to business and deal with the matter in hand: namely Willow's care.

Now Moira smiles. 'Well, the first thing I'm going to do is to make a complaint that Rupert brought Willow to you three hours earlier than arranged, meaning that I could not be here to support you.'

'Right,' I say, with a degree of uncertainty. I'm not sure what this is going to achieve, other than to make Moira feel better. It's a complaint which will probably upset the local authority and could create resentment. Resentment which I'll no doubt end up being on the receiving end of.

It's been a mad, unsettling sort of a day and it's only lunchtime.

By the time Moira leaves, my hangover has abated to a dull thud. On the upside, it does seem as if Willow and Lily are having a lovely time in the sitting room. I return to them to discover that they are engrossed in a game of online

Nintendo Mario Kart, with talk of 'power-ups' and 'battle stadiums'. I hear Lily constantly explaining things in a way which suggests that Willow hasn't played the game before. Given the way Willow is dressed, it also makes me wonder if she was allowed access to games and technology. There is something from another time about her that has a feel of otherworldliness. Perhaps I'm being fanciful: I am making assumptions before I've even begun to get to know her.

The boys get home from school just as I start to feel as if I have regained some order and control in the house. Frankly, I can't be bothered to cook and my body is crying out for the comforting stodge that only chips will provide. A simple solution presents itself from the combination of those two factors: I shall take orders for a takeaway from the local chippy.

Willow is pleased as punch that she's having sausage and chips for tea. I'm going to have to quickly disabuse her of the idea that this is a normal event in the Allen household. We are creating quite the wrong impression about our home on her first day, with ice cream after lunch and a chip shop supper.

I start to slightly regret my decision when I discover that it is far from a cheap option. With Willow there are six of us which means six main meals and, even though we are buying meals only (I don't let them have any cans of drink or extras; we have plenty of stuff in the house), it still ends up costing over £70. Ouch. Since when did fish 'n' chips start costing more than £70? I realise that my out-of-touchness is probably another sign of age.

Jackson comes with me to collect the order. He likes holding the warm carrier bag of food and, when you're hungry, a car filled with the aroma of freshly-cooked fish 'n' chips is the best smell.

Willow is quite happy to sit at the table with us, essentially a bunch of strangers, at dinner. In fact, although understandably quiet, she looks very happy and relaxed. There is lots of chatter. The boys, practised in the art after so many years of foster siblings, are so good at being part of the welcome committee – but Lily is the one who has made Willow feel the most welcome. They are sitting next to each other and I notice Willow watching Lily with a kind of fascination, copying her movements. I suppose we all need cues for how to behave in a new environment, and Lily is most definitely at home here.

As I clear away the piles of greasy paper and put the ketchup-smeared plates into the dishwasher, I think again about the day, and what a weird one it has been. One of those 'change' days when you realise that things are shifting and moving on. I'm in a pensive mood. Moira, I suspect, will become much more open as the weeks go on. I am happy for her. We have been through quite a lot together in the last couple of years and I suspect it won't be goodbye forever.

I'm lost in thought when I suddenly realise that Willow is standing behind me. I didn't hear her come in. New children, unsure of their surroundings, have a way of walking into a room without you knowing, almost like ghosts. Later on, all that changes and you get to know they're coming before you see them.

'Hello, Willow. I didn't see you there. How are you doing? You and Lily seem to be getting on like a house on fire! You've certainly helped her to forget about her tiredness, thank you.'

She smiles.

'Are you enjoying Mario Kart?'

She smiles again. 'It's fun.'

'Have you played before?'

A shake of the head.

'What would you like to do now? Would you like me to help you unpack your bags? Get settled into your room?'

She nods.

'I'll help,' Lily calls from the sitting room.

Good old Lily. We travel up the stairs, carrying black bags as we go. When we get to Willow's room I ask Lily to give Willow a tour. 'So that she knows where everything is.'

Lily is in her element. She's so good at this, she would make an excellent estate agent. I love hearing her talk about the rooms and the house as if Willow was a potential buyer, balancing doors open so that Willow gets the best aspect. The tour will take some time because Lily is extremely thorough.

Meanwhile, I start to remove things from the bags, ready for Willow to put away where she wants. I hate bin bags.

I'm not impressed with her previous foster carer. There is no way I would let a child leave my home with bin bags. If they don't have a suitcase or suitable bag then I always get posh laundry bags so that they can be used again, even if it is by the foster carer or residential home. I recognise the smell of the fabric conditioner. I only use non-bio laundry powder and sensitive fabric conditioner, and this is a distinctive floral scent I recognise. The clothes in the bags are folded and well-ironed. Some care has been taken here. Maybe I judged them too harshly.

From the bedroom window I see Lily in the garden with Willow pointing to everything, every nook and cranny. I even hear her say the words, 'that's a tree.'

Eventually the house tour is complete. When the girls come through the door of Willow's room, I ask where she would like to put things. 'Decision time!' I hold up an anorak. It's neither fashionable nor vintage. It's just drab. She looks at it and makes a very amusing 'sour' face.

I notice that the hair clips have already gone and her released hair softly frames her face. Already an improvement.

'Can I get a new one?' she says.

That has Lily jigging about in excitement. 'Does this mean we can go shopping?'

'Yes, I suppose it does,' I say dryly, rueing again the money we've just spent on the takeaway.

Lily does a reverse fist pump accompanied by a triumphant, 'Yesss!'

There are two whole bin bags full of clothes that Willow decides she does not want. I don't blame her in the slightest. They are dreary, uptight clothes from another age. There are none of the usual teenage 'girl' accessories. There are no hair straighteners, no make-up, no jewellery, no bottles of cheap, stinky perfume, no fluffy socks. No 'things'. Nothing other than sensible clothes and then, as we get to the end, a mouth organ, and a few books at the bottom of the last bag.

I pick up the first of the books and read its title: The *Children's Book of the Bible*. The next one is a lift-the-flap book. Lift the flap? *She's 13*, not three. I'm struck at how babyish the books seem; her foster carers evidently haven't factored in her increasing age. I see the title of this one: *Noah's Amazing Ark*. Ah, right oh. A pattern is emerging. The next one has a red and black cover and is the *Soul Survivor Youth Bible*. That looks a bit more the right age. I study the back. The blurb promises that it will answer tough questions like, 'Why does God allow suffering?' and 'What's Leviticus all about?!' as well as tackling important twenty-first century issues like relationships, terrorism, money. I can't help but wonder quite 'how' it will tackle these issues.

'I'll pop these on the shelf, shall I?' I say. I'm a bit out of my depth here.

She shrugs. 'Do you believe in God, Louise?'

Chapter Ten

Jason

Jason has managed to keep social services at arm's length as much as possible for years. He gives thanks for that, in prayer. And he adores Willow. She is such a good girl. Good at her lessons and good at home. He worries sometimes that she doesn't go out enough, that her life is small. But he's fearful if she goes to the park, and prays that she will come home safe. There are bad people out there. But he'll do whatever he needs to in order to protect his Willow.

Willow spends the time between school and prayers quietly in the living room that also serves as the kitchen. She has been learning to play the recorder along with other pupils in her class at school. She has also managed to get a penny whistle and a mouth organ from the music department. Sometimes she sits for hours playing the mouth organ. Jason thinks she is very good. He wonders where she gets it from. Certainly not his side of the family. Perhaps Elaine's family were musical. He didn't really get to know much about her, looking back.

The teachers at school are used to dealing with him now. They look out for Willow, keep an eye on her, and check in with him regularly. He likes them. The mostly female staff are much nicer than his own teachers were, back in the day. Much more motherly than he remembers someone like his maths teacher, Mr Bradshaw being.

'You're doing a lovely job bringing up Willow,' Mrs Robinson, her year five teacher tells him. 'She's a credit to you. Lovely manners, and always so well turned out, with a crisp, clean uniform.'

They've muddled through for years with the help of the church. One of the ladies helps him with the ironing and the cleaning, and Jason likes cooking. He always makes sure that her lunchbox is full of healthy food.

It's a little worrying that Willow has become so quiet in the classroom, though. The teachers talk to him about that sometimes, about why she might have become more withdrawn over time. She used to be such a confident little thing. But Jason remembers being shy himself at school. It's normal. And she's so talented with music that nothing can be wrong. She always looks so calm when she is playing.

During PE when the children are changing into shorts and T-shirts, Mrs Robinson notices some red bruising on the inside of Willow's legs. When Jason comes to collect Willow he is ready. He knows what to say. He's already rehearsed it. Luckily, the teacher asks out of earshot of Willow.

'Mr Wicker? What happened to Willow's legs? Do you know how she got those marks?'

Jason smiles. 'Oh yes. Willow was playing at the park and was on the seesaw with a girl who was bigger than her and was rocking a bit too hard.'

Mrs Robinson believes Jason because Jason's learning needs give him a sense of innocent honesty. Jason plays his part well because the memory of losing Andrew still haunts him.

He almost believes it, too. Nobody is going to take his Willow away like they once took his brother away.

Chapter Eleven

Louise

I'm ashamed of myself for pretending I haven't heard her question, but otherwise, the first few days of Willow settling in are lovely: relaxed and straightforward. Willow is a polite, helpful, kind child. All in all, a delight to be around, and a totally different proposition from some of the teenage girls we've had the honour of caring for over the years that I've been fostering.

I take Willow and Lily shopping. We make a big day of it and catch the train to Bristol. While Lily and I are engrossed in looking at all the funky clothes, busy holding things up and trying on hats, Willow looks ill at ease. Perhaps puzzled, more than anything.

'When was the last time you went shopping, Willow?'

She smiles. 'I don't remember. Not like this. Mostly Susan chose my clothes for me.'

I know, from all the paperwork, that Susan was the previous foster carer; the one who has made some kind of allegation against Willow. That I will get to the bottom of – sooner rather than later, I hope. But not today.

'Do you know where she got them from?' I'm genuinely interested in where you might find clothes like the ones Willow has arrived with.

Willow shrugs. 'I'm not really sure. Church, maybe?'

Lily is having a lot of fun in H&M and I have to remind her that we are here for Willow. 'Besides which, you've got lots of clothes, Lily.'

Lily switches into TV makeover mode, and begins to style Willow instead. Inevitably, she chooses for Willow what she really wants for herself: in the Urban Punk section. Then she spots a collection of heavy metal and rock T-shirts for bands like Motorhead, Black Sabbath and Jimmy Hendrix. She lights up immediately, in her element.

'Do you like heavy metal, Willow?'

I doubt it, given the bible books and scout uniform, but to my surprise Willow beams.

'Yes, I love it!'

Wow, this is good, I think to myself. That's three T-shirts in the basket. We do well, ending up with three hoodies from the same collection, and three pairs of jeans, one with rips in. That's a couple of months' worth of clothing allowance gone in an instant. The clothing allowance for a foster child is, on average, around £40 per month. That works, just about, for younger children, but it's not a realistic amount for a teenager. At least not if you want that foster child to fit in. A pair of trainers can easily cost £50. Probably more. I learned a long time ago that if I wanted to treat my foster children as if they were my own, I'd have to fund that myself. I have met other foster carers who only get secondhand or free clothes for their foster children. Generally they are not my people.

She looks at the trainers. They go in the basket too. Hang the expense, I shall be only too glad to see the back of those plimsolls. Lily manages to persuade me into buying her a couple of things as well. Both girls are thrilled to bits. I can tell just by the bounce in Willow's step that she is happy with her loot. I am curious, though, at how this little girl from another century knows about heavy metal.

'So, what bands do you like, Willow?' I ask.

Well, that opens the door on a world that I would never have guessed about for Willow.

'Kiss, Judas Priest, Metallica, Motley Crew, Aerosmith-' she begins to reel them off. 'Pantera...'

I haven't heard of the last one, but never mind, I get the gist. The list goes on. She starts to mention individual musicians and then moves on to guitar techniques. She begins an enthusiastic monologue about palm muting, hexatonic patterns and the never ending scale. I haven't a clue about 'sweep picking' and 'octave displacement', but it seems that she does from the animated expressions on her face as she describes them. I can't believe my eyes.

She comes alive, making an air-clench fist and what I can only describe as a 'heavy metal face' while she mimes headbanging and plays air guitar right on the shop floor in front of us. She is like a different child.

'Willow, do you play the guitar?' I ask, when the performance is over.

'I did learn a bit of the acoustic at Sunday school, but Susan wanted me to play the flute, so I played the flute.'

That makes me thoughtful.

As we walk back through town, we come across a music shop hidden away down one of the streets. In the window are all sorts of instruments.

I have one of those moments, completely impulsive. I push open the door and the girls follow me in. I walk up to the assistant dude. It must seem comical and incongruous; he all long-haired rock chic, me all middle-aged mum, but then I thrust Willow forward.

'This girl needs a guitar!'

It's like a scene from a film. The dude in the long rock T-shirt looks at Willow. Somehow, she is not at all phased or embarrassed. In fact, her smile broadens out into a grin from ear to ear.

He hands her an acoustic guitar.

She sits down on a stool and plays the opening to *A Forest* by The Cure. She plays it beautifully, transporting us. But also herself – her face is somewhere else entirely, in another place. She looks so cool.

We all stand by in amazement, especially when she then switches to *Sunshine of Your Love* by Cream.

A couple of the other shop assistants move over towards us, as do a few customers, aware that something special is happening.

'Would you like to try out an electric guitar?' the dude asks her.

By way of an answer she hands back the acoustic. 'Thank you. I enjoyed that. It's a really good one.'

'Have you ever played an electric guitar before, Willow?' I ask.

'No. But I would really love to try.'

This child is incredible.

She slings the strap over her shoulder and the dude helps her to adjust it. Then he stands back to give her the floor. As if to complete all movie clichés, she strums the opening bars to Deep Purple's *Smoke on the Water.*

One of the customers calls out, 'She's a total rock chic!' and whistles.

I have to agree.

She finishes up, smiles again, blushes and hands back the guitar with a gentle, modest, 'thank you.'

We are all in awe.

I'm not entirely sure what it is that we have just witnessed. Willow is thrilled when I say that we can go home with the acoustic guitar. It is as if all her Christmases have come at once. I'd love to walk out with the electric one, too, but the price tag is hefty. I will find a way to explain to Lloyd that she 'needs' an electric guitar. I take a note of what the assistant says would be best for her, after all the staff have finished high-fiving her.

There are high spirits on the train journey home. Willow keeps patting the soft case of the guitar, running her fingers along its neck while we discuss music. I show her some pictures of me that I have saved to my phone: digital photographs of actual photographs of me with my black spikey Siouxsie Sioux hair in a Sex Pistols T-shirt at a Black Uhuru gig.

Lily, an expert in Nirvana, is not to be outdone and talks about all things Kurt Cobain. Willow seems to know everything – every band, every musician, every song. I'm curious as to how she has acquired all this knowledge, especially given the church vibes I'm getting from her at every turn.

She grins and whispers, 'Music is everywhere.'

Beautifully enigmatic, but not helpful in my search to know more about her. 'Were your previous foster carers into music?'

She laughs at that. 'Oh no. Not this sort of music. Only organ music and church music. I told you they made me play the flute, which I suppose I liked for a while. It's a beautiful sound but in the end I found it boring. The teacher, the classical pieces that were chosen, the practising. All of it. I've always loved rock music.'

'So, was it your dad, then? Did he like that sort of music?'

'No, he liked weird stuff, not music. He'd listen to

mainstream stuff on the radio, but he didn't listen to music much.'

She doesn't volunteer any more answers. She's a dark horse, this one, and I think I'm going to very much enjoy getting to know her.

By the time we reach home the men have already eaten dinner and gone to the effort of piling the used plates in a neat stack on the counter by the dishwasher. I will never understand why they can't open the dishwasher door and either put things away or stack the dishwasher and press start. I don't get it. It would almost be easier than this elaborate stacking.

Before I send myself on a spiral of fury and loathing for my beloved boys and husband, I remember that Lily is equally rubbish at this, too. I decide that it is down to me to educate and train them. Maybe when they all have homes of their own I will go around and pile up the dishes, nick their phone cables, leave towels on the floor, put empty packets back in the cupboard, kick off my shoes and leave them in trippable places. Yes, sweet revenge, you will be mine one day. For now, I shall keep my powder dry. My inner witch cackles away inside, plotting future mischief.

Both girls rush upstairs to their rooms to try on their new clothes. Willow is ages in her room, and there is no sign of a fashion show from her. Lily comes down to parade each thing, and looks wonderful in it all. She is becoming increasingly quirky and individualistic in her style, which of course I encourage. 'Sensible' was never my thing.

'What's happened to Willow, I wonder?' I say, when Lily has finished a final twirl.

'I'll go and find out.' She skips upstairs to see.

There is a further delay, to the point where I think something must be wrong. I'm just about to go and investigate for myself when down comes a transformed girl. She is unrecognisable from the child that Rupert brought to our house less than 72 hours ago. A rocker, if ever I saw one.

I look at the two beautiful visions in front of me and beam with pride. How wonderful to be young and on the verge of all that discovery about yourself and the world.

It isn't just the clothes, though. Willow's hair is messed up and Lily has put something on it; it smells like my strong-hold hairspray. The little devils must have been using my stuff. There is a little bedroom next to our room that has a connecting door to our bedroom. It must have been a nursery when the house was first built. That was over 300 years ago; so much has been repurposed since then.

I don't let children in our room, and never have. They have to learn to respect other people's spaces and property. My make-up and hair products are definitely out-of-bounds. But, as with the dishwasher, I have learnt not to feel cross, but to try to think of a way to encourage it not to happen again.

'Shall we head to Superdrug tomorrow and stock up on products?'

Willow grins and nods enthusiastically.

She sleeps in her Motorhead T-shirt. Her earnest nightdress has been discarded and put next to the recycling bins. I suspect we will be back in the clothes shops very soon.

Chapter Twelve

Louise

The boys and Lily have to go to school on Monday, of course. But young Willow does not, because the local authority hasn't approved the taxi costs yet. To drive and collect twice a day from her existing school will cost over £1500 per week. That's a great deal of money and the authority's willingness to spend it that way is somewhat grating, since we get less than a third of that amount to look after a child all week. Moreover, that money isn't going to us, it has to feed and clothe them and fund all their expenses. We don't know how long Willow will stay and what's going on with the courts, but while they're faffing about, Willow will not be going to school.

This is not good. Willow needs to see her friends and have a routine. I check out her school and see that it has a good Ofsted rating. There is absolutely no point in moving her, especially since it could be for a short amount of time. Moreover, it represents a form of stability in a turbulent life.

And most importantly, she has her friends. Or does she? I wonder a little about that. She might invite a different kind of social interaction since she has ceased to present as a member of the former Hitler Youth Party. What was Susan, her former foster carer, thinking? It feels cruel not to let children choose their own style. That Motorhead T-shirt needs to be surgically removed. I shall have a look on Amazon and get her to choose another or this one will need its own feeding bowl.

But the school thing is a problem not just for Willow, but for us, too. Lloyd and I, like many more of the workforce post-pandemic, both operate from home. Somehow, that seems to translate to the social workers as 'not working'. The assumption must be that I am here, sitting on my backside, twiddling my thumbs until they fling out a command.

The reality is that Lloyd and I have very demanding jobs. The irony is that if we didn't do them then we couldn't afford to foster. I will have to seek advice from demob-happy Moira, and consult with Rupert, who has been decidedly quiet since Willow arrived. I know that social workers are super busy, but they do have a statutory duty to check in on new placements.

So, I get on it. I email both with my concerns about Willow's education. Every child is legally entitled to an education so, when the care system is the one keeping a child off school, I do wonder how that sits. Do they send a letter to themselves?

I decide that I will wait for one week to see what happens, and then offer to drive her to school and pick her up for one week while they faff about with their administrative machinations. I'm well aware that this is a dangerous thing to do. Social services will happily let foster carers do these things. Why wouldn't they? The problem is that it will ruin my working day and prevent me from earning the money I need. I have clients and deadlines to fulfil, as well as my commitment to the charity.

I have only recently discovered that, when a child is not in school and it is a logistic problem, such as now – or even if a foster child refuses to go to school, which happens more regularly than you might think – then the foster carer is entitled to a daycare allowance. Somewhere between 60 to 100 pounds a day. I think they keep this information locked up with the nation's other secrets at MI5 as I have never met another foster carer who knew about it.

A few weeks ago, I was asked to represent a couple of foster carers who had been on the receiving end of ridiculous allegations. All were false, but somehow the heads of services decided to take it all the way anyway. I learnt that the wife had stayed at home every day – for 195 days – while a foster boy refused to go to school. The social worker made no attempt to find alternative provision.

I found, buried in the paperwork in teeny weeny microscopic print, that foster carers with this particular local authority were entitled to £60 per day. When I attended the meeting to support the foster carers who, in my opinion, had been treated appallingly, I showed the manager their own policy and said that they owed the couple £11,700. The allegations were swiftly dropped. We are still negotiating on a settlement. My old role as a union rep at the university has stood me in good ground. People and organisations often only get away with stuff because they have not been challenged.

Meanwhile, for this first week, Willow can have some settling in time here at home with us. I will manage my working days around some little outings so she gets to see the area and hopefully feels excited about her future and her life.

It hasn't been long, but from what I have seen of Willow so far, it feels like she is either 'on' or 'off'. When her button is off, she just floats about like a vapour, timid, unsure and shy. Until we mention music. Then she is 'on': full beam and alive. Specifically hard rock and heavy metal, but also rock 'n' roll. Consequently, my new greeting for her has become the 'devil's horns' fists. She loves it and does it straight back. Vincent was the next to catch-on and, even though he's 80s Hip Hop mad, every time he sees her the 'devil horns' are up.

We all do it now. Our household interactions look like a scene from *Bill & Ted's Excellent Adventure*.

I receive an email back from Rupert. I conjure up his image in my mind's eye, and instead of sitting behind a sensible desk, I picture him performing a Eurovision song. I like him, I think, but I'm just not sure how effective a social worker he is or will be. Someone so concerned with fashion and appearance doesn't suggest a selfless soul. I remind myself that Rupert had not met Willow until her placement began to break down one month ago. And yet he feels experienced and qualified enough to describe the way that Willow has an 'insecure-avoidant' attachment style.

I disagree.

I would say simply that she presents as 'shy' until you start to get to know her and go onto her level. Like many younger social workers I have encountered, he genuinely believes what he has been taught in college or university. And, until experience teaches him otherwise, why wouldn't he? Having worked in that environment myself I know that most of the theories that he will have encountered will have been written by white, privileged, middle-aged men. Many of whom may perhaps have been dead for years. And will therefore have had little experience of working on the frontline with children in care.

It's fair to say that I am more than a tad sceptical about all the different attachment theories and labels. I resist saying that a child is categorically this or that. Instead I think children, and adults too, actually, change throughout a day – let alone longer periods of time. That's why I'm so resistant to someone being labelled as having a secure, insecure-ambivalent, insecure-avoidant or disorganised-disoriented attachment style. And that's before I get anywhere near all the other possible learning-need labels that might be applied. It concerns me that we lock children into something that they may just be experiencing only briefly.

So Rupert's assured opinions annoy me a little, although I understand exactly why he holds them. I would just prefer the kindness of 'Willow seems a little shy'.

Because in just a few days it seems that not only has Willow come out of her shell, so to speak, but that she has made good 'attachments' to her new foster siblings. She has excelled in Vincent's master classes on Minecraft and Mario Kart and a few other games. To be fair, I may need to monitor that a bit, though I trust him to keep her away from Grand Theft Auto for the time being. I don't think she needs to learn how to kill hookers just yet.

I'm still very curious about the allegation that has been made against her. It seems exceedingly unlikely that she would be capable of doing anything to warrant such a drastic response.

The end of Rupert's email explains that he is coming at the end of the week to see Willow.

I sometimes wonder what they would do if I said, 'No sorry, I'm busy.' I am, of course, but I will do what I always do and juggle everything around to accommodate our social workers. As will Lloyd. Rupert will not understand that we lose time and money because of his meeting, which is only meant to take an hour but, in my experience, always takes two. He is getting paid for his time, while I am not. We are long overdue for an overhaul of a sector that has 1950s views on women, 1960s theories about children, and 1970s remuneration.

No problem, I shall look forward to seeing you then, I type. And try to convince myself that is true.

I leave the computer and go upstairs to see how Willow is getting on with her room. It is immaculate. Susan, her old foster carer, has evidently drummed into Willow how to be tidy and my word, she's good. Today she has made a neat pile of clothes on the side that I am guessing she no longer wants to keep. She has had the H&M rocker collection on rotation since we bought them. I hold the items up to see if I can send them to charity. Beige shorts and plain T-shirts. Nothing that says, 'I'm young, I'm having fun.' All very clean and sharply pressed. Everything is beige, fawn or biscuit-coloured. A few white and pale blue T-shirts. The pair of black plimsolls, the very same ones that I had when I was a child (which I wore again when I was a young teenager with Teddy boy fluorescent yellow, pink or green socks, this time in an ironic way). Barbara, my adoptive mother, would have loved these clothes: smart, fresh, clean. And as dull as dishwater.

I want to make it as easy as possible for Willow to 'let go' of the clothes. 'I'll just take these away for now, shall I?'

Willow looks up from her guitar for a moment and nods.

I put them in the pile of other clothes by the back door, ready for donating to charity.

I can't get over how easy Willow is to look after so far. It just isn't this way with fostering most of the time. I remind myself that we're still in the honeymoon period. The calm before the storm. And I'm waiting for the outburst. The explosion. The revelation. The emergency.

Something.

Chapter Thirteen

Louise

A few more days pass uneventfully. Willow remains impossibly polite all the time, and she smiles often. When she smiles we see her lovely big teeth as if they are headlamps on full beam, full of brilliance and joy. It's delightful, and infectious. I even notice Jackson and Vincent smiling more than usual.

Willow is bright and naturally curious. Particularly as far as music is concerned. She seems to have a natural 'lean' towards music. I see her bopping about when any kind of music is on. At the table she taps her leg to the beat of just about anything: the theme tune to the *Antiques Roadshow*, the introduction to the news. I have been gradually introducing her to our extensive CD collection. She sits with piles of CDs in her room, listening on the headphones Lloyd got for her, or playing it out loud through the speakers.

Earlier today I got her to listen to Lead Belly. She doesn't mind that it's 'old' music. She is keen to experiment and learn. As soon as I said that he was an American folk and blues singer who was famous for playing a 12-string guitar, she was all over it.

So, her love of music is quite easy to support. And this also feels remarkably easy. Many children come without an interest. It's not that they don't have one, just that they don't know it yet. Often, they haven't been given the space and opportunity to pursue things that interest them. Clearly, Willow has not been allowed to fully express her musical interests, but she was at least allowed to play an instrument, and that has been all to the good and has contributed, I'm sure, to the impressive quality of her untutored guitar playing.

In many ways, I think Willow reminds me of a young me. Although, my interest wasn't music, but art. I was all about the art. You couldn't keep me out of galleries and museums. I pored over books and pictures and spent all my spare time making art. Perhaps I should be grateful for the strict adults and plenty of free time that were afforded to me as a child. Boundaries and boredom can be a good way to create.

Her hair is becoming messier by the day, but that's the look she's going for. In herself, she remains clean and tidy. She is small, and a bit too thin for my liking, but I think that's probably because her diet was controlled.

Perhaps unfairly, I picture Susan with a packet of custard creams under lock and key. A sign in the kitchen that reads *No snacking between meals*. A reminder to 'sit up straight' at every meal. All well and good, but tricky for kids who may have been used to different standards. I'm not sure of her early life, but feel pretty confident, from looking at the referral, that being raised by a father with learning issues must have been hard.

I return to the words in the initial referral. That he *could not keep her safe* and his *parenting was not good enough*. I've heard social workers talk about 'Good *enough* parenting'. It stems from a child psychotherapist called Donald Winnicott who first coined the term 'good enough mother'. I really dislike the phrase. In his definition, the good-enough 'mother' makes 'active adaptation' to a child's needs, which gradually lessens over time according to the infant's growing ability to account for and to tolerate the results of frustration. The idea of being 'good-enough' in his terms is about enabling the child to autonomy. But isn't there so much more to parenting than that?

I have no idea if I am a 'good enough' parent. How do any of us judge that? The children seem alright. I wonder if we can over-egg the pudding sometimes by becoming too critical of ourselves when in fact we're fine. Parents that are not 'good enough' are probably not questioning too deeply the level of their parenting skill. Winnicott explained why he didn't use the term 'perfect' in relation to parenting by explaining that perfection belongs to machines.

But, as foster carers we can be made to feel like machines at times. We can be treated as robots, as though we are devoid of emotion or the ability to become tired. Our work should be about reading each child's needs and adapting our behaviour to allow them to grow, not smothering them by wrapping them up in cotton wool, nor neglecting their needs. We need to meet somewhere in the middle. Exactly where that 'middle' is will be different for each child. And is even a moveable feast for each child. Some days a child feels or behaves as if they are maturing then, the next day, they have regressed. We must not lock them into our expectations but go with theirs.

According to Winnicott's ideas, most children who come into care probably have not received 'good enough' parenting before they get there. Which is why with Willow, and just as I once did with Lily, I need to find ways to go back to the beginning in order to respond to her early life needs that have been missed. I need to do this without freaking her out or creating a dependency.

When I watch Willow, she seems quietly hungry for affection. But it's difficult. I'm mindful that hugs are not always welcome.

I remember post lockdown there was a campaign to go and give people a hug. That got my blood up, since I know that hugs and cuddles can be a dangerous thing. How many adults are still nervous of them after their own early life experiences of abuse? Marketeers can be stupid and naïve. By making ridiculous sweeping statements like 'Give someone a hug', not only are they ignoring the hurt that a significant proportion of the population might feel, they're creating a potentially harmful situation.

We need consent from a child to give them a hug. Of course we do. And obtaining that consent is easier said than done. It needs to be given with openness and honesty. It is easy to coerce and manipulate children. Or teenagers. Or even some adults. We need to be ethical. My recognition that Willow seems to have some 'unmet needs' is not a green light to provide them without invitation. I have to be patient and wait for the right moment.

So far, in the fortnight that she has been with us, she has displayed nothing but happiness here. I'd even go as far as to say, 'joy'. But, bizarrely perhaps, this worries me, too. It's unnatural to be that relentlessly positive all the time. Whenever I go into her room it is immaculate. Showroom-tidy. Not an object or an item of clothing out of place.

Lovely though this is, I'm also slightly perturbed by it. It's a little *too* tidy for my liking, almost as if she is a well-behaved guest and not a child embedding herself into the family. Tidy is not Jackson's, nor Lily's, thing. Vincent, on the other hand, has always been ordered and organised. He never liked a mess or clutter, even when he was tiny. Lloyd and I used to look at each other with a shrug when he lined his Matchbox cars up in perfect order, wondering where he got this sense of precision from. Jackson has always created a mess. The contrast was apparent not just in how they played, but when they ate their dinner. Vincent's area would be spotless, while

Jackson would have food everywhere, sauce smeared on the table and on him. It's normal for children to be different from one another.

But Willow's tidiness is something else. Next level. She is self-consciously tidy, and she does it in a way that I am starting to suspect is to avoid being in trouble.

In my experience, it's after two weeks that the chinks begin to show. Little clashes that reveal the distance between a child's 'before' and the 'now'. Willow is yet to show us any of those chinks.

The only possible concern, and I can't even really describe it as a 'concern' is that a couple of times she has referenced Susan, and the need to not upset her. I'm sure this is where some of the excessive tidiness comes from. I get the impression that she was very strict indeed, and that it was a 'churchy' kind of strictness. Being 'strict' is often about replicating the type of parenting that they themselves experienced. Or, more worryingly, about how to be seen in a community. We never really know what goes on behind closed doors, but foster children – all children – need space to find their own regulation.

Willow doesn't seem to have had the opportunity to express herself until now; to explore who she is and who she is becoming. But she's making up for that here, it seems.

Willow isn't the first child we've fostered to come from a religious background, and I'm well aware that I have my own prejudices on this front. When I was a little girl, my adopted mother sent me to stay with her friends Beryl and David. They lived in Chichester and were deeply religious. They advertised this with giant crosses all over their house. They were very strict indeed. Many years later I was visiting my very good friend Zara who I met when we studied at art school. She also happens to live in Chichester. We were out and about in her car when I had a sudden flash of recognition and realised that we were driving past the house that they used to live in.

Zara knew all about the house, and the family, because their church had been involved in a huge child abuse scandal.

So, my instincts are on alert about Susan and her husband. I realise that I am referring to him in my head as 'her husband' because I can never remember *his* name though it will be somewhere in the paperwork if I check back. Willow never mentions him, only Susan. It's not really fair because I haven't met her, but I'm not sure that I would like Susan very much...

And, once again, I'm torn between the feeling that we have 'lucked out' with Willow or we are on the verge of some disaster. I don't have any grounds for this feeling that we might be teetering on the edge of an abyss or something, other than a kind of instinct.

It's just never this straightforward.

Chapter Fourteen

Louise

What is far from straightforward is sorting out the next steps for Willow's education.

It's deeply frustrating that, even though a couple of weeks have passed now since she first arrived with us, I still haven't had the 'clearance' from Rupert about whether or not I can drive Willow to school. He's 'working on it' and asks me to 'be patient' while he goes through the 'necessary processes'.

Meanwhile, she is kicking around at home while Lloyd and I try to get on with our work.

To be fair, she's no bother at all. She keeps herself occupied, basically listening to music all day or playing her guitar. She sometimes picks up the harmonica. I remember that I used to love playing one of those too when I was young, but she actually gets some decent melodies out of hers – unlike my own tuneless dirge.

Rupert is coming after lunch today. Moira is also going to

join us. Moira, as predicted, is demob-happy. The happiest social worker you could ever meet.

David Bowie is coming from Willow's room. Good choice. It seems a shame to interrupt, but I call Willow down for lunch. I want to get that out of the way before the two social workers arrive. I'd rather not be caught on the hop post mealtime as we were the day that Willow arrived.

A quick sandwich is on the menu today.

'Here we are: now, are you ready to master the art of the Scooby snack sandwich?'

'Absolutely.'

'Basically, you place crisps between the bread. It's particularly good with tomato and crunchy lettuce and mayonnaise.'

Willow embraces the Scooby snack, and we sit munching in companionable silence for a moment. I love sandwiches. Actually, this realisation gives me an idea for dinner tonight: 'club sandwiches'. I've got a set of the cheap plastic swords that help keep the layers together, and some thick chunky triple cooked chips from the oven range in the freezer section. This is an easy meal. I can make a vegetarian version for Lily with cheese and layers of salad. That will bring her some joy when she gets home.

She's not loving school at the moment. Not with those stupid boys that buy into the Andrew Tate rubbish. Girls have a tough enough time anyway, given that 'equality' still appears to be quite a long way off. For example I find it nearly impossible to believe that we still haven't sorted out equal pay for women, despite the fact that women (and men) have been campaigning for it since the 1860s. While I am writing this, the latest figure I can find suggests that the gap in pay is currently 7.7%. When I was working as a lecturer it was 14%, so things have moved in the right direction in a measurable way in the last decade.

Just too slowly.

Back then I had to fight for a full-time contract so that I was able to get a mortgage. Most women were on part-time or zero hours contracts when I began my teaching career. Looking back it was outrageous.

Poor Lily is learning fast that misogyny is alive and well. An irrational fear of women seems to be hardwired through generations of DNA, and results in bullying. But that's no reason not to fight. The fact of longevity doesn't mean it can't be stopped.

I note that Willow is becoming better around Lloyd. She was wary, initially, and I suppose she still is – a little; seeming to find my company preferable to his. She tiptoed round him for the first few days, but seems to have relaxed as more time has gone by. When I'm out with her she seems to move closer to me when men walk by or look at her. Is it society's inherent bias weighing down on her? Or is it a sign that something more sinister may have happened in the past? It's so difficult to tell, and I'm hyper alert because of Lily's recent experiences. Willow's referral made no reference to any abuse of male power in her history as far as I could see. Her father, with his unspecified learning needs, remains a mystery.

Women, especially young women, should be enjoying *their* power, not feeling fearful. My goodness, some girls know only too well that they have power. I certainly knew about my own physicality as a young woman, despite the various abuses that had been perpetrated against me. I would wear miniskirts and short tops. Why not? Girls should be able to wear what they want, but can't because, if anything happens, their clothes choice is thrown back at them. What I have noticed about Willow's clothing choices, since she has been given the freedom to experiment, is that she has begun to dress in an increasingly androgynous way.

When she arrived she looked like she was on parade, in some kind of time warp. Now she looks relaxed and teenage, but with a preference for hiding her shape in loose, baggy clothing. Very teenage, if I don't try to read too much into it.

I have become used to her teeth. They absolutely dominate her face and are a little yellow, perhaps from a lack of brushing, though I'm not sure Susan would have tolerated that — perhaps it's from when she was still living with her father. She's under a strict dental regime here, prompted by myself and reinforced by Lily, who is very fussy about her teeth.

Before I have time to say 'denture cup' the door goes and in floats Moira. I say 'floats' because she really is the happiest social worker ever since her announcement. And she brings biscuits. Not only is she visibly more relaxed, she also seems more thoughtful, kinder somehow, now that she's going. It's fascinating to note – and there's probably some sort of irony that she has become more 'human' as she prepares to depart the service.

'I wanted to get here before young Rupert,' is Moira's opening gambit as she breezes in.

'Oh?' My curiosity is piqued. 'Do you know him?'

'No, but I know of him,' she says, with a mischievous smile playing about her lips.

I don't especially like the sound of this. I need her to be helpful and this attitude might not be.

'Good things?'

She shoots me a playful wink and helps herself to a small plate from the rack for the biscuits.

Okay, I think to myself. This will be interesting.

'Moira's here,' I call up the stairs to Willow. 'Just letting you know. No need to come down yet. I'll let you know when Rupert needs to talk to you.'

'Okey dokey,' she says, leaning over the bannister with a smile. That's definitely one of my phrases that she's picked up. It makes me smile to hear her say it. More evidence of her fitting in and feeling at home.

'And don't forget that he'll want to see your room.'

If I was giving that instruction to any of the others, it would be code for, 'Make sure it's tidy,' but I know that Willow's will be.

By the time I get to the front door I hear Blondie coming from her room. I'm thrilled that she is enjoying listening to music so much. It's wonderful to have something in your life that soothes you and fills your soul with joy and energy.

I open the door to Rupert.

'Hi Louise, how are you today?'

'I'm good, thank you, Rupert. And how are you?'

He kneels down dramatically, almost as if he's about to propose. I'm utterly confused for a moment until I realise that, bless him, he has actually bent down to take off his stark white trainers. I don't remember him doing that last time but then it was chaos when he arrived and I might not have noticed.

'Oh, don't worry, Rupert, you're fine. No need for that here. We don't have carpets downstairs, it's stone, floorboards and tiles. Keep them on.'

He is super jolly. So much so that he seems to physically bounce as he walks through the hall. I note that he has a sheen of fake tan, frosted white tips to his blonde hair and waxed eyebrows. He is a fully groomed young man, who evidently takes a great deal of care with his appearance. He flashes the toothpaste-advert smile at me.

Mesmerised as I am by Rupert's personal toilette, I just about remember to offer him a coffee. He asks for a latte which I know that I could do with our coffee machine, if only I'd read all the instructions. Instead, I do it manually in a mug, heat the milk up in the microwave and pretend.

He pulls a tube straw out of his messenger bag to drink his coffee; no doubt that must be to avoid staining the pearls.

Moira offers Rupert a biscuit which he politely declines.

'All the more for me,' she grins.

I pause for a brief second and think about what a strange bunch has gathered around my kitchen table once again.

'Lloyd will be along in a minute, once his online meeting has finished,' I explain, 'but we can get going without him.'

We cover all the usual starting questions, discussing how Willow has been this week. I explain about the new look and love of rock guitar.

Rupert appears to be stunned. 'Well, that *is* a surprise. I knew that Willow played the flute in the regional church orchestra, but I didn't know anything about guitar.'

'She loves it. Isn't it great that she has that outlet?'

'Yes, quite. Now, what bible work have you done together?' The pearly whites glisten as he waits for me to respond.

Oh dear. I swallow.

I look at Moira who is munching away on a biscuit, saying nothing.

'Um, well, Willow has her bibles in her room, but so far she hasn't really mentioned them.'

I suddenly feel terribly guilty. What if Willow *wanted* to do bible work? Oh my God, I could be failing her, totally unintentionally. And she's so polite that she wouldn't dream of asking. My mouth goes dry and I feel my heart sink into the depths of my stomach. There is no feeling more awful for me than failing a child. I am a tough cookie, resilient and super confident, but when it comes to children I can crumble in a split second. That doesn't mean I'm a pushover, but I do always want to do the right thing by the child.

Moira wipes biscuit crumbs away from her mouth with her index finger. She's so relaxed and happy that I'm almost waiting for her to pull a bottle of prosecco from her bag along with three flute glasses and say, 'Let's get this party started.' I think I really like this version of Moira. But she's not helping me right now.

'Right. But we do all need to respect Willow's religious beliefs. We have assured Willow's father that her spiritual needs will be met.'

In my own defence, I don't see a particular willingness from Willow to engage in devotional activity. Other than on the first day when she asked me if I believed in God, the subject hasn't really been broached. But that certainly doesn't mean that she may not want to pursue her previous faith. When she asked me if I believed in God, I didn't answer.

I didn't know how to have that rather big conversation with a child I'd just met. To say 'no' is too much for most people. Perhaps I have really let her down. I haven't given it much more thought. I'd kind of assumed that the question was a fearful one. Checking that I wasn't going to force her to follow any particular religious path. Some of the things that she has said about Susan I have interpreted in a critical way. But now that I think about it, Willow is so polite that she wouldn't be overly critical.

I start beating myself up. How should I have answered Willow on that first day? I have previously said things like, 'I don't do religion,' when I've been asked that question, but it can sound rude to some. If I try to explain why I feel like that, that can also come across the wrong way. And it's not my intention to be rude about someone else's faith. I just don't feel it myself. Like I don't feel gay or like watching football, or eating pot noodles; it's just not my thing. I think that, given some of the abuses I've seen perpetrated against children over the years, it's difficult to believe in a higher power that would allow that to happen. So I tend to just avoid those kinds of conversations, mostly as a defence against unintentionally offending someone.

Because of that, I'm now fixed on how I could have missed this with Willow. We've tried so hard to respond to the things that she has raised. Letting her choose clothes, buying the guitar. But perhaps I've not been helping her feel safe because I haven't pursued her faith needs. God, I'm an awful person. Not least because I keep blaspheming. I feel dreadful.

Preoccupied by my self-flagellation, I only half-listen to Rupert tell me about the arrangements he has made for Willow to have contact with her father. I watch Moira who also appears 'absent'. She is seriously tucking into the biscuits she brought round. But, at the mention of contact, she shifts back into social worker gear, sits up straight and asks all the right questions.

'I'm sure Louise won't mind driving Willow to the contact meeting.'

I'm about to protest. Usually I'd be cross about being volunteered before I've had a chance to speak for myself, but on this occasion, I don't mind. I'm curious to meet him. I think it's only natural. I suspect most foster carers want to see the parents if they can. It's not just about being nosey. The parents are often the missing part of the jigsaw puzzle. It's also an early opportunity to consider how it might be possible to work with them should we have to.

'At the moment this is a one-off rather than a regular meeting. We'll just see how it goes this time, okay?'

In spite of Rupert's words, I imagine Jason will become a regular contact. Why wouldn't he be?

'So, can you report back on how Willow gets on?'

'Yes, of course I will.'

Moira, perhaps having a sugar rush from consuming nearly an entire packet of cookies, steps it up.

'Let's move onto the important question of Willow's education, shall we? It is imperative that we get this sorted immediately. Willow needs to be at school, Rupert, as you know.'

'Yes. But I'm still waiting for the commissioning department to let me know the outcome of what they've decided.'

'But that's not good enough, Rupert.' Moira goes on to volunteer for me, once again, to drive, so that the schooling can start straight away. 'Louise can then claim the petrol back.'

Well, thanks very much for that, Moira. I can claim the petrol, certainly. But I can't reclaim the time. She has clearly ignored the fact that I have work commitments. No matter how many social workers I meet, I wait in blind hope for the one who doesn't think that we just sit on our hands all day waiting for them to get us to 'jump to'.

Too much sugar for you, Moira, I think. Time to assert myself.

'As you know, I have already offered to do that, but it absolutely must be a time-limited arrangement. I will do it for one week, and one week only. After that, it's up to you. Perhaps you could drive her in, Rupert?' I say, sweetly.

If looks could kill.

Rupert has a copy of Willow's original care plan, and the assessment that was made on Willow's entry into the care system. In her Looked After Child (LAC) medical review, the nurse noted that Willow had redness in both eyes and itching. It was diagnosed as suspected conjunctivitis. I scan over the details describing the condition. There was crustation at the base of the eyelashes and Willow complained of itching. There were also black dots in her eyebrows and on her eyelid. She was underweight and she had six abscesses on her gums.

'No sign of any return of the conjunctivitis,' I say. 'And

we're working on good oral hygiene and a teeth-brushing routine.' I pass the document to Moira. 'I do still think she's a little underweight, but her appetite seems really good and I think she's put on a bit, even in the short time she's been here.'

Moira's eyes change as she reads down the page. She starts to frown. But she's reading the same page I just have. What did I miss?

'Rupert,' she says, sharply. 'Has Willow been *sexually* abused?'

'No, not as far as we know. We're sure that her father has not abused her.' Rupert is quite assured in his response, but does raise a questioning eyebrow.

Moira puts down the paper and pats it with both hands. 'What was the outcome of the reporting of the eye infection?'

Rupert shrugs his shoulders. 'It looks like it was conjunctivitis or eczema. Could have been due to her poor diet or stress. Or a combination of the two. No big deal.'

'I'm afraid I'm inclined to disagree.' Moira's tone is sad. 'When I was in child protection we discovered a number of boys at a school that had been investigated for child sexual abuse. One of the police officers was a sharp chap and he noted that all the boys who were interviewed had, or had reported that they had eczema, which was the explanation given for why their eyes itched and were red and sore. He felt that this was too much of a coincidence to ignore and asked the police doctor to assess them.'

She pauses. I'm still none the wiser.

'He diagnosed them with a different condition. They all had infestations of pubic lice.' There is a moment's silence as I take that information in.

'How did they–' I start to say, before the penny drops.

I take a deep breath in. I reach for the assessment document once more. 'The black dots on her eyelid–'

Moira nods. She's gone from looking like she wants a place on *Loose Women* to looking like she wants one on *University Challenge*. She is a wise old owl.

'Pubic lice in the eye area is a condition that's often misdiagnosed. Understandably, perhaps. But transference occurs between hands and genitals. Touching the face after contact can do it.'

I take another moment to reflect on the fact that it never ceases to amaze me how often misdiagnosis is the reason children do not get the help that they need.

But more importantly, what happened to Willow?

I'm hit by that sinking feeling I have come to know so well. What has Willow been through? She is such a poppet. She is so gentle and kind. My eyes start to well up as I think about that lovely child upstairs who, with her increasingly eclectic musical taste, is now listening to Bon Jovi. I blink back the tears as best I can.

The thought of pubic lice and how they could have ended up affecting Willow's eyes is beginning to sink in. It's a wretched thing to contemplate and I feel sick. I can taste bile in my throat. I'm like a cat on a hot tin roof. I don't know what to do with this information. We agree that we will say nothing for the time being. If she does have an unreported history of sexual abuse then she will need help dealing with that, but there is also a criminal side to pursue. This needs careful handling.

'So I think we can't rule out the possibility that Willow has been subject to sexual abuse,' Moira continues. 'In fact, under the circumstances, I think it's a reasonable conclusion to draw.'

Rupert continues with the rest of his visit as though this revelation hasn't been made, and congratulates Willow on her tidy room and how well she seems to have settled in. I pick up the plates and cups from the table and move towards the sink. I think about Stella, a child that we looked after years ago. She was horribly sexually abused by vile men. I remember how I felt when the realisation of the abuse kicked in.

These poor bloody children. Why do men do it? Not just men. Why do women do it? What is wrong with people? The arrangements for Willow to see her dad have faded into the back of my mind. I will have to check the details against the email that I hope Rupert will send later today. I need the location and time. I will meet Jason, Willow's dad. I hope to God he isn't the one who has abused her. That poor girl still seems so innocent. She is innocent, I remind myself.

My mind is clouded by thoughts of pubic lice, or 'crabs'

in old money. I can't get them out of my head. It occurs to me that I don't know why 'crabs' is used to describe this particular sexually transmitted disease. I look up 'pubic lice' on Google. Oh my God, they are smaller than head lice. No wonder they're difficult to detect and get misdiagnosed – especially when they're not in the pubic area. Yep, under the microscope they definitely look like crabs.

Yuck!

The poor child. I hope she doesn't find out. That would be horrible. But of course she will at some point. One day she may request her file and it will be in there. I suspect it will be factual, written up without much kindness. I begin to wonder if she had them in her private area too. But I suspect she didn't have much, if any, pubic hair when she was still living with her dad. She is small for her age and likely to be a late developer. It's awful thinking like this, but foster carers are pragmatists. We have to be. Over intellectualising and theorising can be left to the 'professionals'. We are the ones who roll our sleeves up and work at the coal face.

I notice that Moira and Rupert stand outside the house by Moira's car for ages after they leave our house. I'm not surprised. There is a great deal to reflect on. Moira's observation could be crucial in unpicking Willow's story.

Chapter Fifteen

Louise

The afternoon has run away with me. Before I know what is happening, the door goes and in come Jackson, Vincent and Lily, one by one. The afternoon routine of bags and coats discarded, most thrown to the floor, begins. Hungry, rampaging children storm through the fridge and all the cupboards, taking ingredients to make sandwiches and stuff crisps in their blazer pockets.

But Lily throws her bag on the kitchen table and yells, 'I hate men!' Her face is a furious red.

'Lily! What the hell has happened?'

Her eyes are waterlogged and her bottom lip wobbling dangerously.

'These blokes shouted out "slut", then "you've got a fat arse" when I walked up the road from school!' She bursts into tears as she relives the moments.

I put my arms around her and pull her tightly towards me. She begins to sob harder with the permission my hug provides.

Lloyd walks into the kitchen, evidently hearing all the commotion. 'What's going on?'

'Go away!' Lily shouts.

Lloyd looks shocked, and then confused. Obviously, he doesn't deserve that, but in the heat of the moment he is just another man as far as Lily is concerned. She weeps through her words.

'Why? Why do I have to put up with this? Why do men do this? I hate them.'

I suggest with my hand flick that Lloyd moves away from the kitchen. He rolls his eyes and puffs out his cheeks – a reaction which isn't helpful at all. His frustration is that this is the exact moment he has chosen to wander in and make a coffee, which is now being denied him. But Lily's emotional state takes precedence over a cup of bloody coffee. He can wait. The world can be a horrible and confusing place and, once again, I'm furious. Why the hell did those idiots think it was okay to speak to a young teenage girl like that? In moments like these I'm surprised that there aren't more women serial killers.

Poor Lily.

I rip off a piece of kitchen roll and hand it to her. When she has calmed a bit, and the snotty tear-stained face is wiped, I settle her down in one of the kitchen chairs and make her a hot drink, together with a peanut butter and chocolate spread sandwich.

I hear myself say, 'Men can be complete bastards.' It's as

if I've been sent back in time to my younger self, revisiting countless conversations with housemates, best friends and students. How many times have I had a female friend sitting beside me in tears, probably smoking a cigarette and sipping black coffee, as they relate the most recent trauma with a man.

'All of them,' agrees Lily, firmly.

Perhaps I shouldn't be stoking this. Not *all* of them. Though it sometimes feels like it. I begin to tell Lily the story of when I met up with an older girl from Oxford who used to live up the road from me. She went to Bristol to do Fashion in the 80s and I thought she was amazing. Her name was Kim and she styled her black hair in big rolls at the front, a bit 50s rock-a-billy, but she was even more glamorous than that.

'And then, a few years after she left for Bristol, I met up with her in London for lunch. I was trying to get into fashion styling with magazines and she was already writing for one of the big glossies. She was so inspiring. She told me how the older women in the business were bitches and wouldn't help the younger ones up the ladder. She took her black sunglasses off to use as a mirror to reapply her luscious pink lipstick. I remember that day that, as we walked through Covent Garden, there were a load of builders up some scaffolding.'

'Uh oh,' says Lily, listening intently.

'Well, as we walked past, one of them called out "Sit on my face!"'

Lily looks at me with such a curious expression on her face. I'm not sure if it's because she thinks I'm too old to have ever experienced such things, or she's horrified that I was once young, cool and foolish.

I continue, 'Kim then stopped in her tracks. I watched her lift her sunglasses away from her face so she was looking directly up at his face.'

'Go on, what did she say?'

'She said, "Why is your nose bigger than your penis?" You can have that one for free!'

Lily laughs. A shadow falls across the kitchen door and Willow appears. She looks a little surprised, perhaps that I've said something outrageous. Lily is used to it.

'Don't worry, we're just taking the mickey out of horrid men.'

'I've just had a bad day,' Lily explains. 'And it means that I'm not loving men at the moment. They're wankers!'

I throw a look at Lily for the language, but I'm not surprised she feels that way given her recent encounters. Willow looks at us both. 'I hate men, too. They're disgusting!'

Lloyd chooses that moment to walk back in for a second attempt at his coffee, but on hearing the words, does an about turn and heads back out again. I'll explain it all later and make it right with him.

'Why do you say that, Willow?' Lily says, through a mouthful of sandwich.

This is the kind of moment when a professional foster

carer turns into Mrs Overall from Acorn Antiques. I become hyper busy in the kitchen in a way that is bordering on ridiculous. There's a very serious patch of something on the worktop that needs furious scrubbing.

Willow screws up her face until she looks like a little rabbit twitching her nose. 'All sorts of reasons,' she says. 'They smell, and they make disgusting noises.'

I don't want to push or pry, but I also really *do*. I don't want to break the spell of two girls chatting. I have that adult fear that if I jump in I might break their line of communication. Willow scrunches her face up even tighter, and brings both her arms up, bent at the elbow, towards her face. Her fists are tight and she shakes her head. It's like a performance piece to represent 'repulsion'.

It makes me think that there is a lot more to it. I still can't get over the pubic lice and what that could mean for Willow. It's creepy and worrying. I would never have even known about the possibility of pubic lice in eyebrows and eyelashes before Moira told us. Bloody awful! I can't seem to shake it out of my mind.

Willow remains like that for a few seconds, then seems to remember herself. She looks up and smiles. 'May I have a sandwich, too?' she asks. 'Like Lily's?'

'Yes, of course you can.' I'm only too happy to oblige and start putting it together, moving the chopping board slightly sideways as I slather on the spread in order to carefully watch both girls without letting them know. Back to being Mrs Overall. But the conversation doesn't develop any further.

I am so sad that life for girls is hard. Being a woman isn't easy either. Especially when I reflect that most women I know are amazing and so capable but still seem to have a raw deal in life. We're not going to square that particular circle today, though.

I place the sandwich in front of Willow. It would be against my religion, so to speak, to actually say Grace before a meal. But I'm conscious of needing to do my best for Willow's spiritual development. I don't like the assignment, but I understand it in broad terms. I clear my throat. 'Perhaps it's a good idea just to take a moment before eating to, um, remind ourselves of the things in life that we *are* thankful for.' There. A non-religious sort of grace. And a way of lightening the mood.

Willow gives me a quizzical look but dutifully pauses for a moment before tucking in.

To further change the mood music from man-hating vitriol, and to continue to fulfil the brief, I try God directly.

'Willow, darling girl, I've been thinking. Would you like me to arrange some church visits for you? Or see if I can find out about joining a local church club?'

She just stares at me. It's a look I can't interpret.

'I just remember that you asked me if I believed in God and I never responded properly. I'm sorry about that.'

She carries on staring.

I plough on. 'So, um, when Rupert was here earlier, one of the things we talked about was whether or not your faith needs are being met. I'm sorry if I've been a bit remiss there.'

She still says nothing.

Shit. Shit. I'm running out of ideas. 'We can go to church this Sunday, if you like?'

That seems to break the spell.

'No. I asked you if you believed in God because Susan did, and my dad did, and I needed to know if I had to pretend to care about God if I stayed here.'

Oh. I'm momentarily confused. 'So you don't believe in God, or you do?'

Lily starts smiling a wicked little smile. 'Willow is a devil worshipper! She can't stop making those devil horns, can she?'

Both girls laugh.

'So you definitely don't want any bible sessions or Sunday school?'

Willow shakes her head, still laughing. 'No thank you, Louise.'

I'm very relieved.

Then confirmation from Rupert that a contact visit between Willow and her father has been arranged comes through the next morning.

I widen my eyes when I realise that it's in two days' time. I wasn't expecting it quite so soon and I don't know what to do for the best. It's not enough time to do a proper build-up and it's too much time to just drop the bombshell and go. Thanks for that, Rupert! I make my feelings known via a quick email, and Rupert's reply is quick. Apparently the timing was a request from Jason's adults' social worker's assistant.

Willow walks into my studio just as I'm making a decision about how to handle it.

I swing my chair around. 'Willow, darling, you are just the person I wanted to see.'

Her face breaks into a delighted smile that goes all the way to her eyes. Those large teeth are good for smiling.

'So, I've got a little bit of news: Rupert has arranged for you to see your dad.'

Her face drops and the smile disappears.

My heart sinks and I jump to what seem to be inevitable conclusions: it must be her dad who is responsible for the lice. What the hell are we doing to this child? Why didn't Rupert actually *ask* her first if she wanted to see her dad before going ahead and organising it?

I reach out and hold her hand, gently pulling her towards me. She leans in and puts her head on my shoulder. I can smell borrowed hair-product from the bathroom that Vincent uses. It's very distinctive because to me it smells of liquorice.

Willow is all skin and bone. Perhaps I was wrong about her gaining weight. She reminds me of a cat that adopted us years ago. We called him Twiglet. He was the fluffiest cat I had ever seen and had the colouring of a snow leopard. But when he jumped on my lap and I cuddled him there was not much there under his fur; it's the same with Willow. She has the oversized Motorhead T-shirt on over a long sleeve T-shirt, but underneath her frame is tiny.

Her arms hang limply down by her sides. She doesn't know what to do and my heart aches for her. I wrap both arms around her and kiss her on the head, gently rocking, like she is a babe in arms. We sway like that for what feels like hours but is probably only a minute or two. She seems calmed and happy in our lovely warm embrace. I wonder how many hugs she has had in her little life. How many from her dad? I cannot help but have a negative view of Jason.

Eventually she straightens back up.

'Do you *want* to see your dad? We don't have to, if you're not ready.'

She nods. 'Yes, I do. I will, if you come with me.'

'Of course I will, Willow.'

I smile and push her hair out of her eyes. 'Now, the other thing we need to talk about is getting you back to school next week. How do you feel about that?'

She looks a bit happier about that piece of news.

I ask her about her friends and her teachers. She seems quite chirpy. No concerns there.

'Now, are you hungry?'

She nods her head. Excellent. I shall take every opportunity I can to put food inside her. She holds my hand out of the studio and along the corridor to the kitchen, as if she is a much younger child. I pull out a chair for her. 'And what would Madam like in today's sandwich?'

She thinks for a moment.

'Could it be a return to the outrageous delight of the chocolate spread and peanut butter special?'

She nods again. I walk around the kitchen gathering up the components to make this culinary masterpiece and, of course, crisps for the crunch.

'What do you think you'll want to wear for the visit to see your dad?' I ask. What I really mean is would she like me to wash her Motorhead T-shirt, because otherwise it will soon need to be surgically removed.

'This T-shirt?' she suggests, as I knew she would.

'You do realise that means I will need to wash it tonight, don't you?'

Lily comes bounding in at that moment.

'Anything for the wash?' I ask. 'And why don't you two go off and listen to some Nirvana?' I seem to remember that being the music they first bonded over. But what do I know?

'Nirvana? No way. I'm listening to Lana Del Rey now.'

I shake my head. Can't keep up with these teenagers.

Chapter Sixteen

Louise

The day of the contact visit soon rolls around. The Motorhead T-shirt is freshly laundered. Willow also wants her ripped jeans and new Dr. Martens ready. I feel like her footman.

'Would you like these?' Jackson offers Willow a pair of earbuds. It looks like a generous donation, but he did get some rather expensive ones for his birthday. Willow is thrilled and I suspect, like Jackson, will soon learn the art of ignoring everything I say because the headphones are on.

She takes them with her in the car, sitting in the front in all her rock gear, plugged in. I'm slightly disappointed because a long car journey is often a good opportunity for some heart-to-heart chat, but Willow is opting for music. Our close proximity gives me a chance to observe her. She seems relaxed enough, in spite of her initial downcast reaction to news of the visit. It strikes me, though, that style-wise she looks very different from when she arrived with us. I hope her dad recognises her.

I have tried not to make too much of this contact. I've treated this excursion as if it is just a trip to the big supermarket.

We pull into the car park at the family centre. It's changed since I was last here. There is a massive factory in the field next to it; that wasn't there last time. It casts a dark shadow over the little building that also looks more 'tired' than the last time I visited. It could do with a lick of paint.

'Ready?'

She nods. We walk through the doors and are met straight away by Jason, standing next to a grey-haired woman of substantive size, dressed in purple tie-dye. I'm slightly annoyed that we have this welcoming committee. In my mind I'd hoped that Willow would have a few minutes to compose herself, get in her zone, but no, we're straight in. Tie-dye is wearing a lanyard. I squint to read what it says. My glasses are in my bag. She sees me struggling and introduces herself as Pauline, Jason's and Willow's contact worker.

I take a long, hard look at Jason. The pubic lice have not left my mind. If it was him who was responsible for the sexual abuse I now believe her to have suffered, I will have to pretend for the sake of the setting that I don't know, but my disgust and disdain is hard to hide because I have a physical reaction. I feel my nostrils flaring as if I'm in some sort of primitive mode, inhaling the dinosaur predator to keep Willow and myself safe.

Jason smiles at Willow and straight away I see where the

teeth have come from. Jason is pale and blonde. I think I read that Willow's mother is Portuguese; that would explain her brown hair and olive complexion. Willow has brown eyes and I can see Jason's are blue, but the teeth are definitely his. There is an unmistakable similarity between them in spite of the difference in colouring.

And, after just a few seconds, I reassess everything I think I know. Instead of a predatory sex pest, I can see that Jason is a vulnerable man-boy. He shifts about on his feet, excited to see Willow. He rubs his left arm with his right hand and folds in on himself. It is immediately obvious to me that he is not capable of looking after a child. He is like a child himself. My only question is how he can possibly have looked after Willow for as long as he did. For years.

'Hello, Dad,' she says, almost with a sigh.

He grins back at her and then walks towards the room where families go to have contact. He sits on the sofa. She sits in a chair next to a toy box. God, this is a depressing sight! I stand near the doorway, where tie-dye Pauline looks as if she is about to bar my entrance.

'Are you happy to come back in two hours?'

I look at Willow, who already looks like she wants to leave.

'No, I'm not. I'll wait here,' I say. I assert myself a little more, leaning into the room to speak directly to Willow. 'I'm outside. I'm not going anywhere. I'm going to sit here on this chair, okay? I'll be here when you need me.'

Tie-dye looks at me with the pursed lips of disapproval, but Willow smiles and clearly feels better. Safer?

My phone is almost flat so there is not a lot to do but think. I like opportunities like this. The luxury of thinking. I like trying to work things out and, if I shift the chair slightly, I can see through the glass and keep an eye on Willow. I can't hear what is being said, nor do I particularly want to, but I have no qualms whatsoever about stepping in if she looks upset.

Despite what Tie-dye might or might not say, my job is to help keep Willow safe, and that is exactly what I will do.

So, I watch. And think.

I observe Jason and I study his every move. He is wearing a silver cross around his neck, clearly demonstrating his belief in God. That must be why Willow went to Sunday school and church, and why she was fostered by fellow Christians. Nothing about him strikes me as 'evil' or 'bad'. In fact, the opposite. He seems like a very kind man. Vulnerable himself, and obviously has fairly significant learning issues. But I also get the impression that he isn't a 'well' man, at least emotionally. He looks lost and troubled, overwhelmed and out of his depth.

Very quickly I can see that this is a difficult contact. The conversation has dried up and Willow is totally disengaged, as is her dad. I'm not surprised, in such lacklustre surroundings. Willow is too old to engage via the medium of toys and books. There doesn't seem to be much 'love' going on, on Willow's side at least. Willow seems neither happy nor distressed to be spending time with him. Pretty soon the meeting becomes stilted and awkward. Willow shifts in her seat, and throws me a look through the window.

I shrug. I don't know that I can just walk in and end it because she is bored and has run out of things to say.

After another couple of minutes, Tie-dye seems to recognise the awkwardness, too. She signals that the visit might come to an early end if everyone is happy. One hour and fifteen minutes before time.

Good job I stayed.

Willow is quiet on the way home after seeing her dad and it isn't because of the headphones. She doesn't wear them. I try, without prying, to gauge how Jason manages to look after himself.

'He has carers who come in daily to check on him.' Willow isn't willing to elaborate. Her tone is almost indifferent. Resigned. She doesn't want to talk about it. She doesn't want to talk about him at all.

I make a decision. I shall take the bull by the horns and make sure that Willow returns to school tomorrow, instead of waiting until the start of next week. She needs something to take her mind off seeing her dad. She can't keep knocking about in our house while the local authority works out if they have enough funds for the taxi.

Ironically, if Willow's attendance drops below 50%, the local authority will act against her parents. In this instance her parents in legal terms happen to be the local authority – and, of course, they are the reason she is not attending. Schools have increasing powers now. If it can be proved that a parent knows that their child is not attending school regularly, and there is no justifiable reason for the non-attendance, then the parent can be deemed to be committing an offence under Section 444 (1) (a) of the 1996 Education Act. If a court found the parent guilty, then a fine of up to £2,500 could be imposed.

There is also the possibility of a short term of imprisonment. Fines are increasingly being dished out to parents, though I haven't heard of anyone actually going to prison for this particular offence. But I like the idea of the local authority having to take themselves to court in this instance.

I will email Rupert and the jubilant-to-be-departing Moira when we get back home, making it crystal clear in writing that I will do this for one week only as verbally agreed. They'll have to sort out the taxi after five days.

The more I reflect on what I saw of Jason, the more struck I am by how greatly in need of support he is. It is a frankly terrifying level of vulnerability. How much more vulnerable while he was bringing up a child? He doesn't look capable of taking care of himself, let alone a little girl.

Why didn't he have help? Why didn't *they* have help?

Chapter Seventeen

Louise

Willow is excited about returning to school. Susan has packed her uniform and it is in good condition, so I am grateful for that.

The morning travel takes about 50 minutes and there are some tedious stop-start moments due to the rush hour traffic. I suspect later in the day it will be around 40 minutes. That still means a daily round trip of three hours. That's quite a hefty chunk of my day swallowed up. But it's only for a week, I remind myself.

I recognise the town where Willow's school is. I've been through it a couple of times and stopped there once to have lunch with Lloyd when we first moved to the area. It seems like a nice locale.

'Do you know where a good place to park is?' I ask Willow as we approach the road with the school in. 'I'll come in with you to make sure everything's under control.'

She shrugs. I reflect that it's not an easy question to

answer if you're not a driver. We drive past the school gates and into a residential area where I see a likely looking cul-de-sac and turn in, hoping to find some good parking spaces.

'No, not here,' Willow says. 'Try over there.'

I think it's an odd thing to say as there are two spaces in the corner, but I do as she says.

Willow is happy to see the head teacher, who comes across as a dynamic and engaging young man. I find myself thinking that he looks too young to be a head teacher. Then I check myself because that's a classic sign of ageing, to think that everyone who is in a position of authority looks younger than they should. I sort of feel as if head teachers should have grey hair. A throwback to my own school days. This fella looks like he could be in his mid-thirties. Nonetheless, he welcomes Willow warmly and she beams back.

I shake his hand and introduce myself. He is friendly and helpful, and on first impressions, the school has a lovely feel to it. There is a nice atmosphere from the moment we enter through the gates. So much so that I daydream for a moment about staying myself. Maybe I could finish off my own school education here. Rather belatedly, but better late than never. I have no qualms about leaving Willow; she seems perfectly happy, so I head back to the car, and home.

I have time to get some work done before I have to leave again at 2.20pm to collect Willow. I make a quick coffee for myself and take one to Lloyd, then sit at my desk and begin working. But because I've got half an eye on the clock, it's not as productive a day as it might have been. It doesn't take long for my mind to wonder. It suddenly occurs to me that in Willow's referral there was a mention of an independent foster agency. I look it up: Strong Foundations Foster Care.

As I scroll through their website I find the 'About Us' and 'Team' pages and see the directors. Two men. I squint and look a bit closer. The caption tells me that one is called *Adrian Butcher*, and for some reason, that name feels familiar to me. I wonder if Willow has mentioned him at some point. Perhaps I'll ask her.

When it reaches the appointed time for picking Willow up, I hang around the school gate trying not to look too conspicuous. I'm well aware that, with the others, the very last thing that any of them would want at secondary school is me waiting for them outside. It sometimes feels as if there's an invisible force field around secondary schools to keep us out!

When she comes into view, I have the chance to observe her before she sees me. I see her chatting to another girl and smiling, relaxed. Oh, this is more like it. Yes, she has been missing this. Education is about so much more than academic results. It will be very good for her to be back inside a circle of friends.

I give her a little wave and she walks straight over, happily chatting about her day as I steer her towards the car.

'I've parked down here. It was the only spot I could find.' We're in a spot in the cul-de-sac from this morning. Willow is not happy at all. A look I can't decipher crosses her face and then she looks down, biting her lip.

I drive off, not able to figure out this reaction at all. 'I don't know what's going on, but I won't park here ever again,' I promise, when it is clear that something about that road has upset her. As we get further away she visibly relaxes.

'Can you tell me what was wrong back there, Willow?' I ask, gently.

She doesn't say anything, just looks out of the window. After another moment, she says, 'Can we turn the music up?'

I leave it for now, not wanting to force anything. But that was a strong reaction. I think again about the undisclosed abuse. Did it take place there?

When we get home, Lily is waiting in the kitchen, keen to find out how Willow's first day back went. Willow nods and smiles, back to being happy.

'Can I have a phone?' she asks, suddenly.

I haven't really thought about this up until now, but she doesn't have a phone, though she is a good couple of years past the age when she might 'reasonably' expect one. It seems to have become the norm on entering secondary school. I'm pleased not to have to have dealt with the issue until now.

Phones are destroying children's lives.

That may sound like sensationalist hyperbole, but much of the research suggests they're damaging in terms of screen time and exposure to inappropriate content, not to mention the mental health issues surrounding social media.

It's horrendous, but governments don't seem to want to do anything about it. I suspect they may be scared of the tech companies. Or, like a James Bond plot, perhaps the big tech companies are the ones actually in charge of the world these days. We've all experienced the phenomenon of feeling like devices are listening in. Everytime I go on Facebook I see a pair of shoes or a linen dress in the adverts. That's because I made the mistake of looking once. These algorithms are very clever. It won't be long before we become the slaves of technology, if we aren't there already. It's scary. So, I guess it's good that Willow hasn't had a phone yet. Perhaps it was something that Adrian and Susan got right. Adrian! That's his name. Adrian Butcher. The man whose photograph I saw on the Strong Foundations Fostering website. Not only was he the director of the IFA, he was Willow's actual foster carer. Now I really want to do some more digging and find out what that allegation was all about. A carer who also runs a foster care agency making an allegation about a child. Wow.

'Good question, Willow. I'm not sure, to be honest. There are all sorts of reasons why it might not be a good idea right now. I'm not saying "no"; you're of an age where it's not an unreasonable expectation. But these things take time to organise. And in your situation it's not entirely straightforward. We can talk to Rupert about it when we next see him.'

There's no real reason to say no. And it will seem unfair

of me to do so. But I know that once she has a phone she will change. She will become absorbed in the scrolling and lord knows what she will be looking at. She has only recently learnt about Minecraft. She is still so innocent of the ways of the online world. I'm not sure that I'm ready for it. Why can't we ban tech from children's lives and let them be children, in the now, in the real world?

I'll delay saying yes for as long as I possibly can. It will be Canute against the tide, but the longer I can hold out, the better.

Chapter Eighteen

Louise

After two weeks it is clear that school is going well for Willow. On one of my regular check-ins with the year head, he reports that she is a lovely, hardworking girl.

'It's good to see that she is continuing to be musically-inspired. She played the flute previously, as I'm sure you know, and was in the church orchestra.'

'Yes, she loves the guitar. Did she have flute lessons through the school?' I ask.

'No, her music lessons were through the church. We can only offer guitar lessons here, that's all. We have a peripatetic teacher who comes in once a week. The days of multiple instrumental music lessons in school are over thanks to the cuts. Do you want me to see if there is space for her to have lessons with that teacher?'

I nod, but wonder about exactly how that will be paid for. Now it seems that it's entirely down to parents and families to fund music lessons. This makes me feel a mixture of depression and anger. Children *should* be learning musical instruments at school, for free, as part of a rounded education. All children should have access to such valuable provisions. Music should be an intrinsic part of the arts curriculum, not just an extra for those who can afford it.

Once again I return to thinking about what we are, collectively, 'doing' to our children. We take away creative opportunities like music education, and we expose them to technology to such an extent that childhoods are eaten up by it. We warn our children about the fearful things like climate change, the danger of online predators and drug gangs operating County Lines.

In the next breath we remove relaxation and joy; those aspects of life and education that would equip students to deal with those threats, like music and art. Music and art then become rebranded as therapies, required to help 'treat' children who have been emotionally affected. Those therapies are expensive. We are charged large sums of money for something that was already there and should be free. Children are exploited at every turn.

Back to reality. There is no point in saying any of this. I just nod again. 'Good idea. Yes, let's look at setting up guitar lessons.' I can't see Rupert authorising payment for them, but we'll cross that bridge another day.

'And we'll see you back later at the parents' consultation evening?' the year head asks.

Ah, yes. My other reality this week is trying to fit in parents evenings for four children. It can sometimes feel like speed dating when we attend these events. The poor teachers look tired before they even begin. They sit in rows and we, the parents and guardians, make wiggling lumpy lines to see them.

In recent years I've noted that the biggest lines are with the core subjects: English, Maths and the sciences. A few in the art and PE lines, but hardly anyone in music. This is depressing indeed, and no sign of it changing anytime soon because parents also no longer see the value in these areas.

Why would they when they are not valued by schools or society at large? Not to worry. Soon we'll all be listening to AI-generated 'fake' music that has an algorithm to appease us.

I tell myself that's enough of the conspiracy theories, and turn my focus back to Willow. Lloyd and I have booked appointments with Willow's teachers for parents' evening. There's almost no need because I'm having such a lot of contact with the school anyway, and I regularly hear how wonderful she is. But attending her parents' evening is about more than that. She also needs to know that we *care* about her education, and this is a very visible way that we can show our support.

Increasingly I reflect that I have never before known such an easy, polite, talented and academically high-achieving child. So very different from the way her father presented at the contact visit. I don't know what has happened to Jason as far as his education went, but Willow has a wonderful capacity to recall information which will stand her in good stead when it comes to exams.

Conversely, my own lack of ability to do this is probably why I was so bad at doing exams. When I actually did them, that is. My mind would drift away from the topic in hand. It still does. I see the same drifting-trait in Jackson too and a little in Lily so perhaps there is no rhyme or reason to it. Vincent has a greater ability to focus, but has a tendency to be a bit lazy – unlike Willow, who is diligent about everything.

I predict that she will go on to do great things.

As I make my fifth journey of the day between our home and Willow's school, I keep driving past the cul-de-sac, even when Lloyd calls, 'Spaces over there, Louise.'

'No, I don't want to go there,' I say, checking the rearview mirror to see Willow contented by my response.

But I can't keep it in anymore. I can't not know. The question comes out before I know it. 'Where did you live, Willow, when you were with Adrian and Susan?'

She looks straight ahead and points backwards.

'In the cul-de-sac back there?' I clarify.

She nods curtly, in a way that says, 'Yes, but don't ask any more questions.'

Well, at least that clears that up. Lloyd raises his eyebrows and I shake my head. We'll discuss it later. But now I have horrendous scenarios in my head about what might have gone on there. What possible circumstances might have led to that strange allegation?

I notice a car park another block away that I haven't seen before. It seems to belong to the local football club. It doesn't look as if there's a match tonight and I can't see any private parking signs, so I take my chances and in we go.

Our walking route back to the school inevitably passes the cul-de-sac. I can't help myself. I'm curious about which house belongs to Adrian and Susan. Remembering the outfits that Willow was dressed in when she first arrived with us, and very much getting the impression that Susan is a little prissy, I decide it must be number three. It's boring, it's tidy and nothing stands out. They have an unremarkable bluey-grey front door and hanging basket outside. You hardly see them these days. This one has cascades of lobelia and petunias in pale tones of blue, nothing too bright.

The more I look, the more convinced I am that, of the handful of houses here, it must be this one. Everything is tremendously *ordered*. The curtains hang equally and there is an ornament in peach and cream ceramic in the middle of the window sill: an insipid thing depicting a woman in a boat with a parasol. We move on quickly even though I'd like to linger, because Willow has walked ahead superfast and is almost at the school entrance. Lloyd jogs ahead of me to catch her up. What happened in that house to generate such a visceral reaction from Willow? She isn't one to overreact or over-dramatise. Quite the opposite, in fact.

The consultation evening is every bit the success I knew it would be. Every teacher praises Willow effusively. I feel so proud of her, and I love looking at the shy but beaming smile she gives at each new morsel of praise. She is so delighted. I make a point of prioritising her best subject: music.

Her music teacher asks us if Willow is playing instruments at home. It's funny the way conversations happen at parents' evenings, where there is a tendency to speak *about* the student in the third person, rather than directly to them, even though they are there and could easily speak for themselves.

'She spends a lot of time playing the guitar, and sometimes the harmonica. But it isn't just the playing, it's the listening. She listens to a lot of music at home.'

I explain that we have worked our way through rock and early punk and now we are studying the blues, soon to move onto jazz.

Willow is enthusiastic about the way I'm demonstrating her music scholarship. Perhaps it's also my knowledge of her.

'And are you still playing the flute?' This is directed at Willow herself. I wonder why this question hasn't been asked of her before in school, since it's also come up with the head of year in discussion earlier in the day.

Willow shakes her head gently and looks away.

'Oh, that's a shame, Willow. You are such a great player. Wind instruments are your strength.'

'Really? That's amazing,' I say.

I learn that Willow has performed in many concerts and

was due to join the schools' regional youth orchestra but her placement ended, and that was that.

'She is a seriously brilliant flute player,' the teacher reiterates.

Willow is small for her age. I imagine her lungs as hidden weapons creating breath like a steam engine. How does this little, interesting girl have so much talent? It seems especially astonishing when I think back to meeting her father. Jason, conversely, seems to have so little in terms of ability and talent. I might be wrong, of course. I'm only going by the notes in the referral and a brief meeting. Jason may have hidden depths. But somehow I don't think so. So many children, both those we've fostered and those we've met through their friendships with our children, seem to be chips off the old block; they even sound and dress like their parents and family. Willow feels like she was beamed up (or down) by Scotty.

I know that we are all 'unique' but she really does seem to be one of a kind. I wonder how this intelligent young woman views the world. It is difficult to tell. She is so gentle and quiet, demure in her demeanour.

'Well, perhaps we'll have to follow that up again,' I say. Inside I'm wondering if the cost of guitar lessons *and* private flute lessons would be prohibitive.

After we say goodbye to the teachers, I have the chance to chat briefly to a few of Willow's friends and their parents. Perhaps unsurprisingly, her friends seem as polite and bookish as she is. I soon find myself with a list of names to present to Rupert to get approval for visits. As ever, I have still not received the delegated authority that gives us some low-level rights to make decisions about basic things like haircuts and sleepovers. If we do not have this in writing, signed by the birth parent, fringes can get very long indeed.

We walk back up the road to the car, still singing Willow's praises. 'All of that deserves a treat,' I say. I can't remember a parents' evening that's been such a delight. Not for my own children, and almost certainly not for the majority we have fostered. 'So, which fast food outlet would you prefer on the way home?'

We are deliberating over McDonalds and KFC when I notice two men. They seem to cross the road very suddenly when they see us. It feels too sharpish to be normal. Both men are carrying books. I'm not close enough to see, but they could easily be bibles.

Willow moves closer to us.

'Go on ahead, you two,' I say to Lloyd and Willow. 'I need to ask Mr Doodah something.' I gesture vaguely back in the direction of the school, and hand over the car keys to Lloyd. He hasn't a clue about what I think I have seen, but I want to satisfy my curiosity.

I cross over the road and follow the men, who head to the cul-de-sac. I wonder if they are going to Adrian's and Susan's. I hang back behind a shrub on the edge of number one's garden, pretend to look at my phone and wonder if this level of surveillance might qualify me for MI5 training.

The men sport smart attire and I watch as they walk up to number five and ring the doorbell. A short, tubby lady in nondescript colours opens the door and welcomes the men in. I can see through their window a gathering of people standing and sitting. This looks very much like a prayer evening. I got the house wrong. Number five's front garden could do with a bit of a tidy up, if I'm honest. Too many dandelions for a smart cul-de-sac like this, and the little half hedge could do with a trim. So, this is where Willow was until a short time ago. I wonder if those men recognised her. They certainly seemed to walk quickly away once they clocked her.

I wonder what's going on.

Chapter Nineteen

Louise

At breakfast, Lily tells me about a group of three boys in her year at school who accosted her yesterday after their maths lesson.

'I was going along the corridor from maths to history and they told me that I should do the world and myself a favour and kill myself.'

This is the last straw for me. Enough is enough. She has been told that she is fat, and that her face is ugly. And now this? I can't understand what the hell is going on – this is from boys her own age. How dare they? How has this kind of a culture been allowed to develop? I call Jackson and Vincent down and ask them what's going on at school.

They both seem to know about this behaviour. Not what has happened to Lily, specifically, but they recognise that this sort of thing goes on.

'It's a thing. You hear it all the time. The popular kids do it.'

'The boys run up to girls and tell them that they're ugly or fat,' Vincent adds. 'If the girls are popular girls, the ones who wear their skirts really short, then they all think it's funny.'

'But the girls are just as bad,' Jackson confirms.

'Yeah, the popular girls are not the fit girls though. They're usually fat and ugly,' Vincent says.

I don't like them using that language, but there is a kind of irony here.

'It's all fucked-up.' Jackson looks sad. 'I was bullied by boys in my year because of my weight.'

'Was?'

'Still am,' he admits.

'Bullying at school is mental,' Vincent agrees.

I feel like crying. What the hell is going on? 'So what does the school do about it?'

'There are safe guarding staff who wear hi-vis jackets and walk around school with walkie talkies, but the bullies know that they're coming so pull kids into the toilets or behind buildings to fuck them up.'

I'm not used to hearing my children talk like this. I'm pretty disturbed by it but I don't say anything, because the look in their eyes tells me that revealing all this to me is a big thing.

Vincent tells me that girls like Lily, who would rather wear trousers, are called lesbians.

'What?'

'Yeah, you're a lesbian if you aren't wearing a skirt up to your arse.'

Surely we've got beyond this kind of categorisation in this day and age? I mean, surely? Isn't this the generation who are more tolerant and accepting than those who came before? Don't Gen Z and Gen Alpha transcend this kind of reductive labelling?

I am a mess. I genuinely don't understand what is happening at school. The government brands the growing number of children who do not attend as 'school avoiders'. But I would not attend if this was the treatment I received.

But I understand now that poor Lily is getting a torrent of verbal abuse in school as well as out of school. No wonder she doesn't want to go out lately. She used to meet her friends and go into town on light evenings and weekends, but she seems to have stopped doing that. I'm not surprised. If a load of 'popular' kids are walking about making inappropriate comments, on top of the white-van men, then this must be terrifying.

And I'm sure this has all got worse of late. It wouldn't surprise me in the slightest to discover a connection between that dreadful man Andrew Tate and his promotion of misogynistic ideas, and the rise of this kind of attack. It's a sick world. We have no idea what our children are watching, or who in the world they are in contact with. This is a ridiculous situation that we simply wouldn't allow in 'real' life. Social media terrifies me.

I am not in a good place today. Usually I just give the children an airy wave from the kitchen, or yell out that I hope they have a good day, but today I see them all out of the door individually. I feel the need to watch them leave the house, and feel nothing but sadness as they enter spaces over which I have no control. One silver lining is that the taxis to and from school are now in place, so I'm off the hook for the daily return journeys. I waved at Willow in the back of her taxi as she went off. At least I haven't heard Willow complain of bullying from school. I try not to mentally add 'yet' to that thought.

We have a meeting with Rupert scheduled for today after school. It's a later start than I'd like but inevitable because of the logistics surrounding Willow's travel from school. By the time she gets home it's usually around 4.45pm, so realistically the meeting won't start until 5pm and it will, no doubt, go on til at least 6.30pm. I've made Moira aware of the timings so that she can attend if possible, and Lloyd has organised his working day so that he can be free then, too. I want to ask a number of questions. And I'm ready for some answers.

The meeting will need the big table so will have to take place in the kitchen, which means I need to have sorted out dinner for the children before it starts. I would have liked a leisurely family meal tonight with time to bond – rather than a rush-job just to make sure that everyone is fed and watered. I would have liked to make it special because I'm so distressed about Lily, and about Jackson and Vincent, and their collectively negative school experiences. It feels almost as if kids enter a war zone each day, except that it's dressed up as this thing called school.

Perhaps it shouldn't be surprising when you imagine 1500 people and all those explosive hormones moving around in a confined space. The way bullying is managed will depend, in part, on the individual teacher. There are struggles in terms of navigating school policies and mechanisms, and dealing with not just the children but their families. If parents stopped saying stupid things like 'hit em, then' or 'tell them to eff off' we might be in a better position.

I don't want to wish my life or their childhoods away, but I'm looking forward to when the children leave school and go to college or whatever they choose to do. School does *not* sound like a safe place right now.

I send emails to all the children's teachers and year heads and cc in the appropriate deputy head. I'm not sure what good it will do, but it at least makes me feel like I'm doing something. I try to do some work but it's difficult to settle with all this spinning around in my head.

Not having to collect Willow should give me a better opportunity to settle into some work, but I only last for about 15 minutes before I'm angry again. Time to take Doug and Dotty out for a walk. A change of scenery, some exercise and some fresh air is what is needed. I feel the calm settling on me almost as soon as I enter the woods. Birdsong is like a kind of balm. It never fails to work, although I sometimes forget to listen. We need to be reminded that the world can be beautiful, too. I'm not out for very long, but it's enough. After a pound around a field I feel much more relaxed.

Rupert offered to bring Willow back from school so that he could talk to her in readiness for the meeting. I wonder if they remembered to cancel the taxi. I doubt it. Not to worry, it's only taxpayers' money that's being wasted. Money that should be going to help children.

It's just gone 4.30pm when the door goes. Rupert and Willow are back in good time. They must have had a decent run on the way home. Willow smiles at me and shoots upstairs to get out of her uniform. I suspect she will want to show Rupert the new her, the 'real' her and I strongly predict it will be the Motorhead T-shirt.

'Coffee, Rupert? Or tea?'

'Not for me,' he says, cheerfully while Willow is still getting changed. 'We had a cheeky Biscoff milkshake on the way back.'

'Nice.'

'Willow seems very happy, Louise, and is evidently enjoying school.'

I agree and feel proud of her once again. And of us, actually. I have to give myself a pat on the back occasionally, because no one else will.

'I spoke to Willow's music teacher. She is really keen for Willow to play the flute again.'

'Yes, we talked about that, too, at parents' evening.'

'I think it would be really good for her, especially as Willow was in the regional schools' orchestra previously. They are about to go into rehearsal to perform a big concert in London and want Willow to be part of it.'

'I think Willow is keener to pursue guitar lessons now,' I say gently. A tiny part of me wonders if this is about Willow or the school.

'And Willow herself is keen to take part,' Rupert continues. 'It would mean music lessons with her old teacher at the weekends and after school.'

I know exactly where this is heading and my heart sinks a little. This additional taxi service will fall onto me. And I'm genuinely not sure that Willow does want to play the flute again. Willow *would* say yes to Rupert and the school, because Willow is a people pleaser. I see it as part of my job to help her unravel herself from that burden. Girls need to be able to say 'No'.

Willow comes down as predicted, in the Motorhead T-shirt. Her hair is much messier, and dare I say, a lot more 'interesting' than when she arrived.

The door goes. I expect it to be Moira, but instead another woman stands on the doorstep. I haven't a clue who she is.

'Hi there, you must be Louise. I'm Carolyn, Willow's new IRO.'

No one said she was coming, nor that there was a new independent reviewing officer, but hey ho.

Next in is demob-happy Moira, smiling and delightfully cheerful.

We head towards the kitchen. Lloyd joins us in the hallway before we get there so we all troop in together, quite the 'party'.

Dotty decides to bark insistently at Carolyn, who bends down to make her introductions and appease the demanding jackhuahua. It actually does the trick and Dotty is quickly calm. We gather around the kitchen table with Rupert seating himself at the head, ready to chair the meeting.

Moira, in another fit of generosity, has brought not one but two packets of biscuits. I find a plate for them. She pushes them into the middle where we all stare at them for a moment before she pulls the plate back towards her and starts to munch away. Perhaps not such a fit of generosity. I'm not entirely sure if Moira is focused.

We work through all the 'celebrations' for Willow. Rupert speaks about Willow's musical talents and informs the room that she will be performing in London soon as part of the regional schools' orchestra. He presents it as a done deal. Everyone gasps at this, apart from me and Lloyd. We're extremely good at silent communication in these kinds of circumstances and I throw him a look which he catches immediately. We both know that it's rare that children in care excel at anything. It's rare for them to go on to university. It's very rare indeed that a looked after child would be performing nationally. So I'm not surprised at the gasps.

My cynical self, however, wonders how much of this is about Willow and how much is about the professionals having a boast. Rupert is certainly lapping up the limelight almost as if he's the one who is going to perform.

The meeting continues and Willow says, extremely politely, all the things that they want to hear.

Then Rupert drops the big one. 'Another piece of good news: Willow is going to have a mobile phone.'

I look at him in shock. 'What?'

'Yes, my manager and I have decided that it would be a good idea for Willow to have a mobile phone.'

We haven't discussed this yet, and he says it all in front of Willow, making it impossible for us to disagree.

Lloyd says, 'Right. Erm, ok. We weren't expecting that. Who is providing the phone?'

'You. It can come out of the allowance.'

Now, he's broken another golden rule here. Social workers should never talk about allowances in front of the children. It is impossible for a child who has never had to run a household to understand that the allowance is to pay for food and bills and clothes.

When a child hears the word 'allowance' they think of a pot of money just waiting to be used by them for whatever they want. Without running a household, how could they have any idea of the costs involved in adding another person to the outgoings. The casual way he has dropped this in is outrageous.

I am seething. Again.

Because it comes at the end of a day that I began by seething about bullying. It's not about the allowance, or the fact that he's made the decision. It's far more fundamental than that. How the hell are we going to keep Willow safe? She is completely innocent of the ways of social media. She has no idea about online safety. And we're now going to be responsible for educating her. I feel outflanked.

Rupert clearly set up with the school to do flute lessons without consultation with us. Fine. But as for the phone, that's completely different. I know Willow wanted one, but surely it isn't as simple as that? There must be a few hoops for her to jump through first, and conditions surrounding its use to be discussed? Some ground rules established. But the nature of the meeting makes all that impossible.

As to what I would perceive to be the important business of the day – Jason – and how Willow feels about the contact, thus far, no mention.

I decide to raise it. 'Did you manage to talk to Willow about her contact visit with her father? How it went and how she felt about it?'

No he hasn't, he has to admit, and has the decency to look a bit sheepish about it.

The IRO rescues the situation and asks the classic, 'What are your wishes and feelings about seeing your dad again?'

Willow shrugs. Standard young teenage response when sitting in a room full of adults who are, frankly, bordering on the cusp of ridiculous.

I try to firm this up by asking a very direct question. 'Is Willow having contact with dad again?'

'It was reported by the contact worker that the contact was uncomfortable,' Carolyn says.

Phew, I think, now we can drop it for a while.

Rupert pipes up, 'So, we'll arrange another visit again in a month's time and see how that one goes.'

I can't get this lot out the door fast enough. Alas, they seem to think that they can hang around after the business of the meeting has concluded to chit chat.

No way, I've had enough. I stand up. 'Okay, lovely to see you all, but now, I'm afraid, we need to get on and sort out dinner.'

They take the hint.

'Oh, that wasn't a hint,' Lloyd says with a wink after they have gone. He laughs at my exasperation. But not at the mobile phone bombshell. He, like me, knows all too well what giving a child in care a mobile phone means.

Chapter Twenty

Louise

Rupert tries to arrange it so that, despite Willow now having a taxi to collect her from school, I should in fact collect her on Tuesday in order to take her straight to her flute lesson on the other side of the town from where her school is, wait outside for an hour, then bring her home. In real terms that amounts to approximately three hours of my working day.

He is beginning to grind my gears.

I am irritated by his total lack of awareness. He hasn't a clue about the strain that this will cause. He also says, 'okay yeah' at the end of each stupid sentence he utters, which winds me up even further.

When he 'tells me' that is what I will be doing, I am firm.

'No, I'm afraid that doesn't work for me. Tell you what, why doesn't Willow walk or catch the bus? Or you arrange a taxi to her flute lesson, then arrange a taxi to bring her back after her lesson?'

I have no doubt he will bitch to his manager and say

that I'm being difficult. I can just picture the scene. With pursed lips she will say, 'It's Louise Allen. She can be very outspoken, I'm afraid.'

This is just one of the reasons we are leaving the local authority. If, as any normal human being would, you stand your ground in response to a stupid, ill-thought out idea, you get a reputation for being 'difficult'. I think this is exacerbated because I grew up in care myself. For some reason, I think that is threatening and invites a defensive reaction from any insecure or mediocre social workers. And of course, they have all the power. I want to work with an agency with whom you can have a straight, honest conversation and they won't look like they're going to cry. Our work is with and for children, so it's frustrating when the *adults* sometimes behave like children. It feels a little bit as if Rupert has been given the talking stick and wants to get on down with the kids. It is so dangerous.

He should *never* have gone behind our backs and agreed to Willow having a phone without any safeguarding plan put in place. Thankfully, we have managed to stall the actual acquisition of the phone, but I'm not going to be able to do that for very long. I'm just delaying the inevitable.

Once Willow's participation in the orchestral concert is confirmed, rehearsal and practice ramp up. I have to take Willow to additional flute lessons on a Saturday and Sunday too. For two months that means another three hours or so on both weekend days. I know it's only eight weeks of my life, but I start to begrudge it when I have so much to do at home: the washing, the cleaning, making the beds and so on. Not to mention spending some proper time with the other children. I haven't even got time to walk the dogs properly. That's what I really resent. I should be able to enjoy walking my dogs. That's the best 'me time' in my week and is the main way that I get some exercise.

The first Saturday morning of rehearsal, Lily decides to come with me to keep me company and kill some of the time while Willow is in her flute lesson. We wander around some of the local shops for a while but there isn't a great deal to see and we pull up with a good few minutes to spare before Willow is due out of her lesson.

I take in the house: nice and neat, but dull and unremarkable. I go to the door to knock and wait. On arrival we were running a little bit behind so Willow went in on her own. The door opens and an older woman stands in the hallway, with Willow in the gloom behind her. She looks like the epitome of a teacher from a few decades back: neat and matronly.

She seems friendly enough, if a little brusque.

'How did it go?' I smile.

She replies with a few things in fluent flute which go completely over my head.

I smile again. 'Sounds good. Thank you very much. We look forward to seeing you again tomorrow.' This is a lie, because the last thing I want to do is drive back here again on a Sunday, but a necessary platitude in oiling the wheels of communication.

Sunday comes around. Lily doesn't accompany me this time. The shops were boring yesterday and everything is closed on a Sunday anyway.

While the Saturday lesson is in the morning, the Sunday lesson is late afternoon. Mrs Flute Teacher attends church in the morning. Willow doesn't seem to be overly keen on going into the house today. She leaves quickly, too, and goes straight to the car at the end of the lesson, without bothering to wait while I ask the 'how did it go?' questions. It's unlike Willow to be impolite, but Mrs Flute Teacher does seem to have a rather austere manner.

I also notice the silver cross dangling over the top of her pale blue blouse. I didn't notice it yesterday. Perhaps she is connected with Willow's old church. I suspect, too, that she knows Willow's previous foster carers. I wonder if she also knows what happened, and if she is aware of the allegation made against Willow. It's not exactly a question I can easily ask.

I still don't know what happened to her, but *something* did and I can sense that it was not good. There are no accurate records, and that is partly because a church authority was involved in the initial placement. That can be for the good, but not necessarily. All groups and organisations are made up of good and bad. To quote Stevie Wonder and Paul McCartney, *there is good and bad in everyone*. But they go on to sing that we *learn to live when we learn to give each other what we need to survive, together alive.*

Songs and lyrics like that should be able to change the world, but they don't. They are nice sentiments that might change perceptions for a split second, then people are back to being people.

My curiosity about the church's involvement is growing because there are several components to this. Willow arrived with two bibles. I have never known a child come into care with a bible. I have recently attended training about faith to do with asylum-seeking children. That resulted in us putting ourselves forward to look after refugees, but instead, after buying prayer mats with sewn in compasses to point to Mecca as advised, we received no children at all. In my head I think I had imagined long queues of evacuees: young children seeking a loving home away from war-torn environments. But, thus far, we have never looked after a child from a faith background and, to be perfectly honest, I'm not feeling the religious 'buy in' from Willow.

The music she loves, for starters, doesn't feel very Christian. (I'm thinking of those devil horn fingers again!)

But she did arrive with those two bibles and other Christian tracts.

On the other hand, she also had foster carers who made an allegation about her – but there is no trace of the content. One of the ex-foster carers is a director of an Independent Fostering Agency, Willow's dad was, and maybe still is, a member of a church. The school wanted Willow back in the orchestra but that was about the school. Mrs Flute Teacher may be connected to the church, judging by that silver cross. I don't imagine it's a fashion accessory.

In the car Willow blasts ACDC at decibels until we get to McDonalds where she orders a McPlant meal and a strawberry milkshake. She's not vegetarian, but trying them out because Lily likes them. She is quieter than usual. I tell myself that it's just the pressure of the looming concert, but I have a funny feeling about all this. I can't put my finger on it but something isn't right.

And when my woman's instinct says something isn't right, it usually isn't.

Chapter Twenty-One

Louise

A couple of weeks go by. Smoothly. Willow continues to be a lovely presence in our home. She has definitely put on a bit of weight and looks altogether less angular. Her face is fuller and healthier. Unlike some other children we have fostered, there are never any problems around hygiene. She is a wonderful child, almost preternaturally good. She dutifully goes to school with never a murmur of complaint and all we hear is praise. She gets emails and postcards congratulating her on various achievements, and there are never any issues about homework. This is brought into sharp relief by Jackson, whose teachers I seem to hear from regularly under slightly different circumstances. It seems that he would rather hide under his duvet and game than meet deadlines and complete homework tasks.

It does feel to me, though, as if Willow is sometimes working *too* hard. School work and flute rehearsals dominate her evenings. She is very good indeed, but I don't think I hear the love in the playing. She is rather mechanical about it. The guitar is heard less and less, because that is Willow's 'fun' instrument and there doesn't seem to be much time for fun.

So the request for a phone has become a way of rewarding her for all her hard work and achievement.

And the phone is the part that I'm not happy about.

I am rewarding Willow who has, in my opinion, been coerced into taking part in a concert that she does not want to be part of, with a phone I never agreed to, that will inevitably be paid for with my money because that little teeny weeny allowance will not cover it. I wonder quite how we have ended up here. Could I have stopped any of this from happening? I'm not sure.

I can't wait to leave this authority. Soon I will be as demob happy as Moira.

On the plus side, I genuinely feel that Willow is so happy here. We all love her. She is a gentle presence in the house, and she is naturally kind. Her musical talent is incredible, although I can't help but feel that her gift is being exploited by the powers that be for their own glory.

Jackson and Vincent, having evidently decided that Willow is working too much and too hard for an average young teenager, or at least one outside Dickens' books, have invited her downstairs to play Mario Kart.

Jackson is always good at hosting and has made up a number of bowls of sweets and popcorn to accompany the gaming. His intention is admirable, though I spot him taking handfuls as he pours.

Vincent is busy on tech stuff, arranging the furniture to facilitate maximum gaming comfort. Lily, who wouldn't usually engage with anything the boys have initiated, is making noises that suggest she wants to join in. Willow is encouraged down by Jackson.

'All work and no play makes Willow a dull girl,' he jokes. 'Come on, I'm not taking "no" for an answer.'

There is actually no resistance from Willow this time. The sound of her practising the flute in her room stops. I hear her light step on the stairs and, after a few more minutes I hear laughter and loud shouting from the sitting room. Gaming does something to their volume buttons, I think. Nevertheless, it's good to hear Willow enjoying herself. Much more like what childhood is meant to encompass. I am not cut out for being a tiger mummy. I am far more interested in seeing children smile.

While they play, Lloyd and I enjoy dinner for two in the kitchen, Thai fish cakes, boiled potatoes with lashings of salt and butter and steamed green beans. Delicious.

The atmosphere outside the house begins to change. As if someone turned on a tap in the sky, down comes the rain, quite suddenly. Straight shards of angry water pour down on the house. We both frown, and it isn't just being slightly disgruntled at a change in the weather. Where we live, a sudden downpour is a little more serious.

Like everything else: children's social care, or adult social care, or the NHS, the education sector, you name it; the flood systems all started to come unstuck 30 to 40 years ago. The town floods when it rains like this because the farmers stopped clearing the ditches and began planting above quota amounts of maize – a crop that sucks out all the nutrients from the soil until it can no longer absorb the rainwater. Instead it just runs off the land, down the lanes and into our lives. The highways' drains can only take rainwater from the road, not all the water that comes down from the fields. When that happens, the drains can't cope and all sorts of nasty things come out of the drains and can make us ill.

Although, as I think about it, that is quite a good metaphor for what's happened to children's social care. In this scenario the social workers and their managers are the farmers and the maize growing is the commissioning of private services which has spiralled entirely out of control.

The dark clouds suggest that this will be a little more than a quick shower. We put down our cutlery and head towards the hallway to put up the flood gate. I prop up the sandbags and close the door.

Back to our dinner. And a continuation of the good metaphor. The flood gate enables us to get on with our lives safely and prevents more stress, damage and expense. The same as in children's social care. Let's use Willow's case: the flood gate, the 'prevention' could have been the intervention of earlier and more targeted support for Jason, Willow's father. Was that what the church was doing? Thought it was doing? Wanted to do but wasn't able to? I know wonderful people in our community who are from different church groups who genuinely do good work and help people. What am I missing?

Because something went wrong somewhere for Jason and Willow and the rainwater permeated anyway. Willow ended up in care.

What went wrong?

Something simply does not add up.

But the matter of Willow's phone becomes more pressing. Lloyd checks with Rupert what phone he has in mind for Willow. He puts Rupert on speaker so that I can hear too.

'What phones do your children have?' Rupert asks.

'Well, they're iPhones, but they're not new or high spec. We gave our children our old phones when we upgraded.'

To my surprise Rupert says, 'Then Willow should have the same.'

'An iPhone?' Lloyd says, incredulous. But I detect a hint of anger creeping in.

He's right. She absolutely shouldn't have one. How are we going to afford another iPhone for starters? I am also perplexed at the decision that we should casually give a child who has only recently discovered Minecraft, has never had a phone before and is completely ignorant of social media, an expensive smartphone.

Lloyd is fuming when he gets off the call. 'Guess what the eldest child suggests for Willow? An iPhone 13!'

Eldest child? That's quite funny for Lloyd. If Rupert *was* my eldest child I would have given him a dressing-down by now. He's been thoroughly spoilt by his manager who, it seems, can't be bothered to 'manage' him at all. As the 'corporate' parent, Rupert's is not the best parenting model I would choose to use.

Lloyd is really unhappy about all of this, and so am I. Very unhappy indeed. In the past, the phone has been at the root of all the behaviour problems with a child. If not their phones then their parents' phones or their friends' phones. Perpetrators were invited in droves when we began to give children phones. Steve Jobs had children but obviously didn't care about all of ours.

I text Moira with my concerns. She fires straight back. If that's what he says. Mrs Demob has lost her mind as far as I'm concerned.

I have the flute lessons marked in the calendar and enjoy crossing them off. A kind of a countdown to when I'll have my weekends back. Six more weekends to go. I have tried to encourage Lloyd to do some of the heavy 'lifting' on a Saturday and Sunday, but he has politely declined my invitation. His justification is that there is so much work to do on the house that would cost a fortune for someone else to do. My weekend time is obviously cheap or free by comparison. I try not to take the bait on that one. And one of us has to be there for the others who want feeding and watering regularly. No doubt he throws a bone into the cage occasionally.

He does, though, take responsibility for buying the new iPhone, doing all the research and sorting out the contract. It is an eye-watering sum of money.

After school on Monday we present Willow with her shiny new iPhone 13.

The others look on in amazement, if not with a little envy.

I knew this would happen. They all want new phones now. Imagine the cost. I am firm. 'No, and I've already explained that this is Rupert's idea, not ours.'

'Can I change social workers, then?' Lily quips. 'I need a new laptop as well as a new phone!'

'We might have to discuss the meaning of that little word "need", Lily.' I tell her quite clearly that she is not to rinse children's social care.

'Yeah, but a girl I know in residential care got her carers to pay for her tongue and belly to be pierced,' she laughs. Then flicks her fingers to make a cracking sound as she informs me that they have indeed been 'well and truly rinsed'.

Another thing I'm not happy about: children being given what they like, no questions asked, with public money. I have to advocate like crazy to get anything officially for Lily or Willow, but the children have learnt how to 'rinse' the system. Another wave of relief washes over me knowing that we will be leaving the local authority soon.

Willow disappears off with her phone, and with Vincent,

who loves an instruction manual. He is so like his dad in that regard. Jackson, on the other hand, is like me. He will *possibly* read the instructions, long after they were needed, and when the point of no return has been reached in the attempted setting up of whatever piece of equipment it is. That's why I needed to be married to Lloyd before I bought anything from IKEA. I would be crying tears of hopeless frustration if it were left to me.

At least parental controls have been put on the phone; that reassures me somewhat. We used it to try to book a table for dinner at The Boar, a nearby gastro pub and a parental control warning came straight up. I also tried to book a table at a pub called the Cat in a Hat. The same thing happened. Perhaps it was something to do with the names of the establishments. It's good to know that providers have a block on bestiality. Phew! We're all saved.

It doesn't take Willow long to forget Motorhead and ACDC for the new excitement of kittens and dogs doing silly things. It happens within a few short hours. Every time I turn around she's standing next to me with the phone screen pointed at my face saying, 'Aww, look at this one!'

As with all the children, all devices have to come downstairs at bedtime. There is a row of phones, iPads and laptops lined up on the kitchen counter. It looks like an unofficial repair shop in one of the side streets. In the morning, she rushes down to retrieve it, and then takes the phone in the taxi to school so that she can be on it for the duration of the journeys there and back. On Tuesday, when she comes home, she goes straight to her room. By Wednesday she is like every other teenage girl, lying on her bed scrolling.

The addiction takes hold quickly. She is soon obsessed with the phone. I feel so much frustration and anger. I knew this would happen.

'Try not to worry too much, Louise.' Lloyd tries to comfort me. 'It's the novelty. She'll start to regulate herself soon, and get back to being more balanced again.'

I admire his positive outlook, but I'm not so sure. When I'm out and about I watch girls walking down the roads staring at their screens, oblivious to their surroundings. It's a way of not engaging with the world, and who knows what the hell they are looking at?

Within a few short days I feel like I've lost Willow. I was just getting to know her and now, all of a sudden, she's 'gone'.

We try to carry on as usual at home, but the boys find it impossible to draw Willow back down. Setting up the sitting room as a gaming empire no longer cuts the mustard now that Willow worships at the Apple temple. I think they feel a little hurt. They have worked hard to make Willow feel welcome in her first few weeks and now they have been 'dropped'. They like foster siblings who are fun.

I'm careful to write it all up on WhatsApp, the latest way to record fostering logs with young social workers. I'm just waiting for the day when Rupert tells us that he is setting us up with a TikTok account. It was just a few short years ago that foster carers were reprimanded for communicating with each other on WhatsApp. Now the social workers are actively encouraging us to do it. Love life!

At the weekend when I drop Willow off at Mrs Flute, I see such a shift in her mood. She is more than reluctant to go in. She has tentatively tried 'stomach ache', 'headache' and 'sore throat' this morning as a way of avoiding the lesson. At my raised eyebrows she has gone in. Is it the lure of the phone that's done it? If I'm honest, I'm a little intimidated by Mrs Flute. She may be little, and the first word I think of when I picture her is 'prissy', but somehow she commands authority. Consequently my inner 12-year-old, the one who was trying out Silk Cut and cider down the rec, is afraid of her. Five more weeks until the concert, then we never have to do this again.

In my hopeful moments I can believe that Lloyd is right: Willow will come back from the iPhone wilderness she currently inhabits and join us once more in the present. I know it's on trend to be mindful and live 'in the moment'. I'd take a fraction of a moment from Willow right now.

When we get back from the lesson, I dart about picking up the washing from the individual little mounds outside the children's rooms where they couldn't quite make it to the official pile at the top of the stairs. I have to do it all in double-quick time since my domestic day has been curtailed by the lesson. There isn't much from Willow. I guess that her fascination for the phone has prevented her from bending over and picking up the laundry. I shake out a pencil sharpener from a pocket. It must be meant for the bin. It's broken and useless: the blade is missing.

In the middle of the night I wake up with a headache. It may or may not be loosely connected with the two glasses of red wine I had earlier. I look at my bedside clock. It's the early hours of the morning, just past 2am. Too long to try and survive until daybreak. I sneak downstairs to get some paracetamol and a glass of water. While I have my back to the sink to take the tablets I look around the kitchen in the semi-gloom. I look at the little family of devices nestling in their charging station, idly wondering what their net worth is, especially given the cost of Willow's new iPhone.

Which is when I notice that it isn't there.

Chapter Twenty-Two

Louise

The next morning, I resist saying anything to Willow. I'd like to give her the benefit of the doubt. She's not a natural rule-breaker. She may have fallen asleep. That's quite common. Sometimes the other children have faked being asleep so that I don't take their phone away. Lily, especially, has done that a few times, curling up to face the wall so I have to lean over her to locate it. It's a position that makes it really difficult for me to fish the phone out of her bed. Never underestimate the Ninja skills of a teenage child, especially a girl.

I speak with first-hand experience. How many of us pretended to be at one friend's house when we were actually at another friend's house, somewhere we shouldn't have been? With my parenting hat on, I still have to remember the young person I once was, and remind myself that I can't and shouldn't expect to control everything. I've come to understand that sometimes a little freedom is healthy. But I'm going to watch this situation with Willow very carefully indeed. I can't help but feel that Rupert has basically thrown an extremely naive child to the wolves. Those algorithms are there to make money. Let's not kid ourselves: most people who are interested in making that kind of money are not always blessed with a developed social conscience, no matter how many trees they might claim to plant. All children are vulnerable to the power of algorithms but, hopefully, most children have been raised by loving, sensible adults who have trained their children to use their phones and warned them of the pitfalls of social media. I know that schools do their bit, but things move on so quickly, and the reality is that the buck stops with the parent or carer.

And the parent or carer needs to be continually on their toes: I learnt only recently that children can put all the stuff they do not want you to see in a fake app that looks like the calculator in order to hide things on their phone that they might not want an adult to see. A tool which effectively creates a hidden space on the phone. It's a quick and easy way of ensuring that uninformed parents and guardians can't keep track of what their children are looking at.

I had to work really hard on Lily in order to help her to manage her phone properly. And I really do believe that children in care are more vulnerable and susceptible to the phone's seductions.

From a foster caring perspective, an annoying reality is that if the phone is the child's, meaning the birth parent paid for it, then despite who pays the bills, you can't take it away. Phones have made fostering and adoption (which has become more like fostering with no support these days), incredibly difficult and sometimes impossible. I find that most social workers, despite their age and ability and interest in the phone, will still adhere to their manager's policy which results in the formality of a box-ticking exercise.

As an example, we had a situation recently where a child absconded and it required the intervention of the police. When they returned, we were told that we had to take the phone away at night. Except that we had already asked the social worker to help us enforce taking the phone away at night when that proved challenging. They, frankly, couldn't be bothered.

We operated in the nonsensical realm of 'shutting the stable door after the horse has already bolted' and ships that have 'already sailed'. Agreements were drawn up, or some other nonsense, that we knew was too late to implement but, because they had messed up initially, they had to cover their backs. So, we were left to 'enforce' something that they hadn't, and the onus and blame for the failure was on us.

It's something of a hobby-horse of mine, but the Children Act was written just a few years *before* the tech boom in the early 90s. There is nothing but a flimsy bit of individual local authority guidance on how to look after children with phones, which these days is pretty much all children. I find it difficult to believe that as that piece of legislation was going through parliament, the clever clogs lawyers and government ministers and 'think tanks' (or as I like to call them 'think tins') didn't know the digital tidalwave was coming. Or that it hasn't been meaningfully updated since.

What I do know is that, without doubt, I can feel a tangible difference between the pre-phone Willow and the one who 'exists' in our house now. Before, she was so *present*, so alive, so into her music. She acted and behaved like a child in the moment, experiencing the world. But now she's disappeared into the web of misinformation and swiping.

I feel that I have lost Willow, just after finding her.

When she got into the taxi in the morning, I used to be treated to a smile and a wave. Now she is head down and straight on her phone before the driver has pulled away from the kerb. It's got a grip on her.

I wave anyway.

After they have all gone I do my usual house rounds, flinging open windows and pulling back duvets to air the beds. I pause to wonder, briefly, why there are so many crumbs in the beds along with socks. I pull back Willow's duvet and find a broken plastic school ruler and another broken pencil sharpener. There are a few bent out paper clips too. What on earth is she doing to be so careless with her stationery and equipment?

After the beds I whip back around the upstairs rooms to do the bins. I don't do them every day, but now that they all take drink cans and meal deals upstairs, if I don't do it regularly their rooms can smell like the inside of a student's microwave. I tip each bin out and separate the contents into two bags: one for recycling, the other for ordinary waste. I tip Willow's bin into the white plastic bag and notice tiny blood dots on squares of toilet roll. Maybe this has something to do with her periods, or a nose bleed. Or perhaps she's squeezed a spot too hard. I have noticed that she's developing a good set of spots recently. It's a shame, and annoying because her diet is excellent. Or at least it was.

She seems to have adapted her eating style to that of a fully-fledged teenager in recent days. I no longer see the fruit going in the way it once did and, if I'm honest, she's looking a bit thin again. More like she did when she first arrived. But she could be between growing spurts. My sons seem to get thinner during and just after a growth spurt, before building up to the next one. It's a complicated business, all this growing.

I pick up all the washing I've gathered and head down to the kitchen. More separating, this time into piles of the darks and lights. Out flick Willow's two cute kitten hair clips that she was wearing when she first arrived. It looks like one of the cats has fallen off the metal clip. I'll fix it with a little dab of adhesive. Maybe she's feeling a little sentimental about Adrian and Susan. I don't know, but it won't hurt to make that quick little repair. I reach for the superglue, then leave them on her chest of drawers in her room to dry.

I need to send a few pressing emails for work. Rachel and I need to write a new business plan for Spark Sisterhood, my charity to help girls leaving care. The trouble is, the boundaries and scope seem to keep shifting. The government, or at least local governments, seem to be making it harder and harder for families to access money that they are entitled to. Our current preoccupation is with foetal alcohol spectrum disorder (FASD). More and more children have FASD than the professionals, including the GPs, realise. Misdiagnosis for ADHD and autism are not helping. They are labels which describe the way the brain processes, but FASD is a form of brain damage. I recently read the shocking statistic that 45% of prisoners in New Zealand's jails have been diagnosed with FASD.

Children here in the UK and around the world are not getting the support they need.

Of course, the best thing would be if women didn't drink or take drugs while they were pregnant but that's an impossible dream, or at least a ridiculous idea. So many women drink a little through pregnancy. FASD can result from a relatively small amount of alcohol at the wrong time of the baby's development.

Many mothers who drink alcohol, especially in the early stages of a pregnancy, have not yet realised that they are pregnant. Some mothers suffer with addiction and, instead of getting the support that they need to manage that addiction, they are stigmatised and censured. Once again we put the blame at the mother's door. Perhaps a solution would be to stop selling alcohol. I can't really see a world in which that would ever happen. Instead, as a society, we are left to mop up the fallout from FASD without adequate resources with which to do so.

Poor children. None of them asked for this.

With the benefit of hindsight and new research, I can see that my own adoptive mother looked and behaved very much as if she had FASD. Her mother was certainly well acquainted with gin, but Barbara was born in 1926 – not a time when much thought was given to the foetus.

All these things churn around in my head as I think about how to approach the business plan for the best. Things seem to shift almost week by week as we learn of more issues for girls leaving care. I spend the rest of the day working on it. At least it keeps me from worrying about Willow too much.

Saturday rolls around once more. I get up early, very aware that I need to get Willow over to her flute lesson later on this morning and there's a lot to do beforehand. I'm conscious that I haven't heard much practising going on in recent days.

When I ask her how it's going I get a 'fine' and a dismissive shrug.

I don't press her, partly because I'm fairly convinced she was pushed into this by her music teacher, and by Rupert, who I think just wants an opportunity to boast about *his* success rather than enjoy Willow's for its own sake.

I finish cleaning the kitchen, sort the washing, peg out the wet washing, squeeze in a little gardening and dash to the shops. I can do a bit more of the shopping when I've dropped Willow off at her lesson. When I get back it's time to take her. But when I call her down to get into the car she has completely forgotten about the lesson, engrossed instead in watching some nonsense on her phone.

'Got your flute?' I say, when she eventually comes to the front door.

I know she hasn't because she's empty handed. Back we go, into the house to fetch it. I'm late now and know that we need to get on the road or Mrs Prissy Flute Pants will give me one of her scary looks.

We are five minutes late by the time we pull up outside the house. I reach into my bag to check my phone, only to discover there is a message from Mrs Flute cancelling the lesson. It was sent at 9am. I have not looked at my phone all morning. I look at Willow and let her know the news.

She does a fist punch in the air and says, 'Yessss,' like she's just scored in a cup final. I reach to turn the engine back on, look up and see Mrs Flute outside her house. She is with another woman. I feel stupid for being here but I don't think she's seen me. I say to Willow, 'Look, there's your teacher.'

She glances up from her phone, and nods. 'That's Susan with her.'

I check that she means her old foster carer.

'So, they know each other? Susan and your flute teacher?' I say in a way that Kojak might have, just without a lolly pop.

Willow looks at me like I'm a complete idiot. 'Umm, yes, of course they know each other. They're all in the same church.'

I pause to process this.

After another moment she says, 'Can we just go, please?'

I start the engine.

At home once more after our wasted trip, Willow disappears straight back upstairs. I don't try to stop her. I think I'm becoming resigned to the absence of Willow, swallowed up by her phone. To be fair to Lloyd, he's right: Lily disappeared when she first had her phone and it took a while before she began to come back up for air. I will have to think back to the boundaries I put in for her then. Now she has sort of self-regulated and only uses it *nearly* all the time, not all the time like Willow. So, I try to live in hope. I make coffee and tell Lloyd about seeing Susan.

'What did she look like?' is his first question.

'Well, I'm not sure we should be judging people on their appearance,' I say.

He shoots a raised eyebrow in my direction, knowing that this is exactly what I do all the time.

'I mean, I'm not entirely sure that we're even allowed to describe how people look anymore. We can't comment on people's appearances without being offensive.'

Lloyd throws me a 'don't be so woke' face, so I fess up.

'She is short and round and looked very square.' I hear the words coming out of my mouth and laugh out loud when

I realise I've just described a child's early years shape-sorter toy. 'That's all I can tell you, your honour.'

The rest of the weekend goes by without incident. Willow is polite as ever, but decidedly disengaged. I keep reminding myself that she is a young teenager and, when they are that age and despite them living with us, they do disappear. And teenage girls are different from teenage boys.

It's Monday before I know it, and I still didn't manage to do all the work that I wanted, even with the cancelled flute lesson – which only saved me an hour in the end but might have saved me three if I'd looked at my phone. I don't know if it's my incompetence or I'm over-committing myself. I'll choose the latter because it's less depressing.

I see the children off to school, though my efforts are mostly ignored. Vincent is the only one who actually says goodbye. When the others leave I just hear the front door go. I wave goodbye to Willow as usual. She is in the back of the taxi on her phone, but does manage a dismissive version of the royal wave with a low hand, while not lifting her eyes from the screen of her phone.

I turn around, head back in and give myself a 9am deadline to have stripped the beds, picked up the washing from the top of the stairs pile and all the bits that never made it as far as the pile. The circle of life.

I am winning today, and easily make my target. Standing next to the washing machine I unravel the bedlinen ready for a good wash. Out drops another broken ruler and my small nail scissors from the bathroom. There are little blood stains on her bed sheet.

Uh oh. I think I know what is happening. We've been here before, with other children.

How have I missed this?

I think back to the broken pencil sharpener I found and discarded without a second thought. I know the answer. It's because I just didn't expect it from Willow, given how wonderful and polite she was initially – and so I let my guard drop.

I give myself a good talking to. It's time to get to the bottom of this, Louise, I resolve.

When Willow arrives home from school I encourage her into the kitchen using the lure of custard donuts, It's a success. The others, having arrived home a good hour before Willow, are already upstairs with their donuts. I realise, too late, that none of them took plates. A conversation for later I think.

'How did you feel about seeing Susan on Saturday?' I ask, when Willow has a mouthful of donut to keep her occupied. It gives her a moment to think.

She makes a face. 'Alright, I guess.'

'Did it feel weird?' I try to dig a bit deeper, albeit gently.

She looks into the middle distance and makes another face.

We're not getting very far here. To avoid delay and the risk of the others coming in to break the moment I dive right in. 'Willow, what *was* the allegation that they made against you? I need to ask. What was it that you did that was so bad?'

Her eyes pool with water and tears begin to spill down onto her cheeks. She wipes her eyes with the back of her hands.

Jackson appears at the door, behind where Willow is sitting so she doesn't catch sight of him. He looks as if he is about to barge in on the hunt for more donuts. I surreptitiously rearrange my expression into 'clear off', and he disappears immediately. I sit down opposite Willow so that I can still see the doorway. Not for the first time I rue that the last owners of the house took the door off to make it more open plan. My phone is on the table, in reach.

'I'm listening, and I don't want us to be interrupted. Can I just send a text, just quickly?' I hold her hand, give it a squeeze then text a message to Lloyd: *Please tell everyone to stay away from the kitchen inc you. Willow needs to talk.*

What happens next changes everything.

Chapter Twenty-Three

Louise

I put the phone down and go back to holding her hand.

'It's okay, Willow. Whatever it is you have to say, it will all be okay.' I'm trying to be reassuring, but the first rule of disclosure is not to promise that things will be okay, because I can't *know* that. So I qualify it as best I can. 'You know that you are safe here, and you know that we love you and care about you.'

More tears spill from her eyes.

'Can you tell me?' I go back to the question. 'What was the allegation made against you by Adrian and Susan?'

She sniffs, hesitates, then mumbles. 'They said I stole some of Susan's jewellery.' She shakes her head. 'I didn't, though. I really didn't. I promise I didn't. I wouldn't.'

I believe her. I can't imagine Willow taking anything that doesn't belong to her.

She checks to see my reaction then sniffs on, 'I didn't understand why they were accusing me. I was just told that

I had done something really bad and, instead of the police getting involved, they moved me. They said it would be better that way.'

I keep hold of Willow's hand, conscious that I need to keep digging here. I have a courtroom's worth of questions here. What jewellery? Where was it supposedly taken from? If it was expensive it would have been on their insurance and they would have had to have reported it missing to get a crime number. What would a young girl with no previous criminal activity, or even any hint of the potential for it, come to that, want with jewellery that belonged to Susan?

'I'm sorry, Willow.'

I *am* sorry, and I'm also not convinced by any of this at all. Moreover, it feels disturbingly like a situation that once happened to me. I wrote about it in *Thrown Away Child*, my first book. Barbara, my adoptive mother, set me up *twice* using a stolen jewellery theme.

Once when I was in her bedroom, cleaning, I picked up a ring and tried it on and looked at myself in the mirror of her dressing table. I remember looking at myself in the glass and noticing a figure move from the landing. It was obvious that someone had seen me. I put the ring back. I was accused of stealing it. I had not. Barbara put me through several weeks of hell, and no one stood up for me. She told people in the community that I was a thief. I was so ashamed, despite the fact that I had not taken it. I was shut in my bedroom as a punishment, with a tray of bread and water left outside my bedroom door, treated like a convicted criminal from the Victorian times. Then, just like that, it suddenly reappeared.

The other time was when I was playing around a friend's house. Barbara didn't like that. She never liked me socialising. Looking back, I think she would have seen the fact that I was in the company of another mum as some kind of threat. She sabotaged the play date by accusing me of stealing a ring. It was just a cheap piece of costume jewellery, like something that you would have found on the front cover of a comic or magazine, and I came home with it on my finger. I simply forgot to take it off because she came early to pick me up and we were rushing.

Instead of reminding me to give it back to my friend, she told me that she was calling the police. I was terrified. In the end she made me walk up to my friend's house and knock on the door and hand the ring back and apologise. My friend's mum was dumbfounded, but I didn't read her face properly at the time because I was so ashamed and scared. I do remember her saying, 'It's only a cheap plastic ring, don't worry, Louise.' Barbara was lurking by the front garden gate. I was ashamed of her too.

So, this story that's now creeping out about Willow stealing jewellery just does not sit right with me. It doesn't add up. It feels wrong. Willow has not got a bad bone in her body, and her plea that she wasn't guilty hit home.

I'm desperate to know more, but I also don't want to push Willow any more about something that she clearly finds deeply upsetting. And progress has been made: she's confided in me. I'm not impressed with Susan and Adrian at all. I know I'm only hearing one half of a story, but that's not how you deal with things. Jewellery is easily lost or mislaid. What if Susan was responsible? Willow taking the blame would be the easy route. What if they had been burgled and didn't know it? What if, what if!

I'm ill at ease about this because I have such vivid memories of Barbara trying to frame me, trying to put me in a bad light. I remember the overwhelming feeling of shame most of all. With Barbara it could have been to cover something up, or that she was genuinely bonkers. Both, I suspect. So I feel for Willow. I remember that feeling – especially if, like me, she did not actually take anything.

Poor girl.

'Can I tell you something else?' Willow sniffs.

I nod.

'I don't think I really want to play the flute in the concert.'

And there we are. I knew it.

'What made you agree to it?'

'I don't know.'

'Whose idea was it?' I gently push Willow about who was involved and why she agreed.

It transpires, though I'm not surprised, that the school's music teacher is the connection with Mrs Flute Teacher. I wonder where Mrs Flute fits into the stolen jewellery incident. Was she aware of the allegation? I wonder if Susan told Mrs

Flute that Willow was a thief. I wonder if that is part of the reason that Willow hates going. I can see why she wouldn't want to return there. The injustice would leave a bitter taste. Maybe the atmosphere is difficult. I don't know. Willow doesn't really talk about the actual lessons. I just know that she doesn't seem to like going and can't leave fast enough. Why put her through all this just to be in an orchestra? It doesn't seem right at all.

I email my concerns and thoughts to Rupert and Moira, telling them about Willow's disclosure and asking Rupert for more information, although I'm not holding my breath for a helpful response. Moira has gone down somewhat in my estimation as she winds down towards her departure. She just seems to be less focused than previously. But I have to give her the benefit of the doubt. She has surprised me before.

The silver lining about her going is how much I enjoy watching her in meetings lately. She is supremely entertaining as she so obviously couldn't give a hoot. Now that she is no longer looking for a climb in her career in children's social care, she has gone off the boil somewhat. Perhaps that isn't surprising. No doubt she will be a great wedding planner if they can keep her off the champagne and macarons.

Rupert's reply comes back quickly: he will look into it.

He can have a look at any time he wants, so there need not be any delay. I'm not going to be told that it's really hard to find out details. Willow has only been in one other placement, an allegation of such gravity as the one from Adrian and Susan will be clearly on record somewhere, with all the gory details.

To my surprise, Rupert comes back a few minutes later again and asks about our availability for a Microsoft Teams meeting online. Moira will prefer that, I'm sure. No one will be able to see what she's really up to, or help themselves to one of her precious biscuits. So, just like that it's booked in for the next day.

I tell Lloyd. 'Do you think we can do the meeting in your room? Your monitor is huge and I hate being cramped up in front of my laptop.'

When the children have all gone to school the next day, I make two coffees and take them into Lloyd's office. Douglas and Dotty follow me like little minions and look decidedly put out when I close the door on them. Lloyd doesn't like them in his office. Dotty gives a little plaintive whine just so that I'm in no doubt whatsoever as to how sad she is about this arrangement. No doubt she and Doug will lie down outside his door until the meeting is finished then follow me to my studio where they have their day bed.

We start the meeting with the usual pleasantries, Rupert doing his best to assert himself and mansplain more about Willow's character and behaviour. Because of course we have no idea about that given that we are actually living with this child.

Lloyd gives a gentle tap to my ankle with his foot, out of

view of the camera. His way of saying 'stand back, Satan.' Since we all watched Greta Gerwig's *Barbie* movie, and mansplaining was outed in the Allen household, the boys are forbidden to do anything like it. Lloyd has been on a short leash ever since on that subject. When a whole community (by which I mean half the population) have finally been given permission to be annoyed by a hardwired behaviour from the other half of that community, there is no coming back from it now.

There's no getting away from the fact that Rupert has a very annoying manner, as far as I'm concerned. He comes across as arrogant, which is never an attractive quality, but is just not appropriate in a social care role.

I wish he would stop saying 'it is what it is' and 'we are where we are'. He isn't to know they are among my linguistic pet hates. I find them so defeatist. It's like saying we can't be anywhere else and it could never be any different. As for 'okay' as his punctuation mark of choice, that really drives me nuts.

Lloyd, sensing my impatience, scribbles on the pad next to me.

You just don't like him. That's not his fault. Give him a break.

It's true. He is, as they say, 'wet behind the ears' and that grates when I have been doing this for so long.

Because Moira is on screen, I have no idea where in the world she actually is. She's got that weird backdrop that makes it look like you're in a hotel lobby in Dubai. She's probably in the car park at Tesco's on her way to doing a bit of shopping, and why not? It's a little discombobulating though.

I want to talk about Willow's cutting, but something in me decides to minimise this, as I don't know what Rupert will do. Sometimes the corporate parent is a complete idiot and goes from zero to a hundred with nothing in between. Frankly, it can seem as if they are more scared of Ofsted and their insurance policies than anything else. I choose my words carefully, framing it so that I don't over-dramatise.

'Willow has been experimenting with scratching.'

That covers it. It will be recorded, officially, so that we could not be accused of being ignorant, stupid foster carers if she ends up in A&E because she's cut an arm off. At the same time, it won't be enough to feel too alarming. It's the magic tightrope of balance that we must walk between trying to keep the drama out and away from the child. I often compare the vast leviathan of children's social care as a slow-moving beast. By the time they have written it up, had a few meetings and come up with a safeguarding plan, everything has moved on and probably been forgotten about. This is one of the special treats of working as a foster carer: you are always damned if you do and damned if you don't.

Rupert's arrogance is no doubt borne of ambition. I resolve to tread carefully to protect Willow. It strikes me that she never asks after him and, I suspect, therefore doesn't see him as an ally. Or perhaps she doesn't take him that seriously at all; he's not anywhere near her style tribe. I think he's much more S Club 7 than ACDC. Time to shift this conversation on.

'So, perhaps we can now move to the subject of the allegation?'

Moira sits up. She will have a view on this, especially since we have had several spurious allegations over the years from mischievous children, some notably taking inspiration from their birth parents.

'Sure.' Rupert says.

'What was the allegation about, specifically?' I ask, even though I now know the answer. I want to hear the official version.

'Willow stole some jewellery.'

'Did she?'

'What do you mean?'

'I mean, was this theft ever proved?'

Rupert looks puzzled. 'What do you mean?' he says again.

I say it slowly. 'Was this allegation proved?'

He looks baffled.

Moira steps in. She can tell, even via a screen, that I am onto something. In spite of her recent lackadaisical approach, she is a woman with a good heart and has been a genuine advocate for children. 'Rupert, Louise's question is very clear. I'll repeat it. Has this allegation been proved? By which I mean, is there evidence? Was it investigated? Were the police involved?'

Rupert reads his screen whilst we stare at him. Eventually he says, 'No, it appears that the police weren't called, because the carers wanted to protect Willow.'

'Right.' I jump back in. 'Then there is no evidence. Which means that there is no case. It is their word against Willow's. How do we know that they didn't get it wrong? Or make it up?'

Rupert is flustered. 'Well, of course they didn't just make it up. They are good, church-going people.'

Before Lloyd can kick me, I jump in and say, 'How do you *know* that? Just because that's the image they choose to present to the world is no reason to accept it. You don't know what happened. If this hasn't been fully investigated, how do you know you aren't being fooled on a basic principle in child protection?'

Lloyd, sensing victory, also joins in now. 'If it was an expensive or sentimental piece of jewellery, they would have wanted it back. It stands to reason.' He then slips into his 'reasoning pose' of sloping shoulders and steeple fingertips. 'It's not your fault,' he begins. 'I'm assuming that you didn't write the initial report?' He starts blaming the person who wrote up the allegation. 'You have explained that there was no attempt – of any kind, it seems – to investigate the allegation. Whoever wrote this allegation up sided with the adults, without taking Willow's version of events into account. That doesn't sound very balanced to me. Willow could be totally innocent and yet she has a nasty big blot on her reputation because the adults automatically believed the adults. What happened to being presumed innocent before being proved guilty.'

He's right. But he's arguing it much more coherently than I would. I'm overwhelmed by how unfair this is and that means I would be arguing from the heart rather than the head.

We watch Rupert try and retain face while Moira smacks him in it, metaphorically.

'I think, in the absence of any actual proof, Willow's records ought to reflect the fact.'

'Er… I'm not sure—'

'I have some other important issues to bring up,' I say, while Rupert is still floundering on the back foot. 'Such as the fact that Willow does not want to continue with flute practice.'

Rupert looks shocked, and then disappointed. 'What? She really doesn't wish to pursue the flute? I find that hard to believe.'

When Moira reminds him that these are the wishes that she has expressed and therefore the decision to end the lessons is 'in the best interests of the child,' it seems that the flute issue is a done deal.

Onto the next thing on my list. 'Willow has also asked when she is seeing her dad next?'

'The fact that this has been left so open-ended is quite unsettling for her.' Lloyd backs me up again.

'Um, I haven't gotten around to arranging that yet.' Rupert is on the back foot. 'After the reports from the last meeting we're still deciding if Dad and Willow should have contact.'

Because they are clearly the ones that know best, obviously.

When we leave the meeting, I look at Lloyd. 'How did our lives come to this?'

We both genuinely feel a little bit sad that we ever became a fostering family. It is so much hassle and beset with obstacles.

Then we do what we always do: find a way to do our best for the child. We have to transmit some sense into a system that sometimes has none.

As soon as Willow is home from school I break the good news to her.

'I've had a chat with Rupert. He's agreed that you no longer have to go to flute lessons.'

She beams at that. And then a moment later, her face falls. 'But how will I tell my music teacher?'

Bless her. She hates to disappoint people.

'Don't worry. Rupert has the task of informing your music teacher at school.' Well, he is the corporate parent after all. 'You don't need to think about it or the concert any more. Put it out of your mind completely.'

Willow is thrilled and straight away looks physically lighter and happier in her face and body, as if the proverbial weight has literally been lifted from her.

I think she is looking a little too light in the body though, as a general observation. I am keeping a closer eye now on what food she is eating. I need to be sure that she is eating enough.

I wonder when a good time would be to talk about the things that I'm finding in her room. She must realise that I find broken rulers and pencil sharpeners and blood dotted toilet roll when I'm clearing up.

Of course she knows, or she would have hidden them better by wrapping things up and disposing of them in the big kitchen bin. If she was smart then she could even use the community bin just over the road. And she *is* smart. So, I reason, she must *want* me to see it all, because that way she is letting me know that she needs help.

It must be terrifying to do that to yourself. And to know that you have the power to do that to yourself. I need to get a good look at her legs or arms or wherever it is that she is cutting herself. I've told Rupert that it's just scratches, but I don't know that. I need to find a way to ascertain the severity. Are they cuts that will fade, or are they deep cuts that will permanently scar?

And how do I go about finding out?

I think about doing a Google search for suggestions, but I know that if I do that I'll fall down rabbit holes that will make me worry more than I already am. The best thing to do is to find a way to take the drama out of a situation. This is good advice for my own response, as well as for Willow.

Because I'm very worried. My trusty intuition rarely lets me down. Intuition is telling me that something isn't right. I think back to Moira's revelation about pubic lice. There has been some kind of abuse here. My instinct is based on my own childhood abuse. I know that, and I do my best to be objective. Boys are more likely to be sexually abused when they are young, but girls can be abused at any time, and are particularly targeted when they are adolescents. I have looked after a few boys who were sexually abused and it was heartbreaking. Not just the emotional damage, but the long-term physical effects like needing reparative anal surgery when they are older. Girls can also require surgery after having objects pushed into their bodies. Girls are so vulnerable – and we still live in a world that hasn't quite shaken off victim blaming. I feel so mad at the world sometimes.

I take a sharp intake of breath when I think of Lily being called a prostitute by an old man as she walked home through town. It might be the thin end of the wedge, so to speak, but how dare they!

I know, though, that I need to tread very carefully indeed. Sometimes, those who are responsible for protecting our children don't want to hear ugly truths. I've already been on the receiving end of dismissive attitudes from social workers. Once, in the past, after I shared my conjectures with regard to an experience of a child, not dissimilar to Willow, the social worker wrote in her casenotes: Louise is on a crusade.

Something has definitely happened to Willow. She is going through puberty, preferring to look a bit like a boy. On its own it doesn't mean much. I'm certainly not trying to suggest that all girls who choose a more masculine-presentation were sexually abused, by any means. I am the first to embrace any break from the shackles of gender imposed by social conditioning! But it's a reasonable hypothesis when combined with the conjunctivitis/lice revelation.

And, once again, I have personal experience that makes me take notice of these things. My adopted mum dressed a bit like a man; other kids used to tease and bully me at school because of the way Barbara looked. She had short hair with a side parting, a rugged face, never wore any make-up, always dressed in trousers with a checked shirt and lace-up shoes. Her own history was tragic.

Not only was she abused by her own father, her alcoholic, unemployed musician father, for his own satisfaction, she was also sold by him to other men for sex. This was during World War II. She gave birth to her youngest brother when she was 12 years old.

The vile doctor sewed her up too tightly, perhaps with a sense of righteous vindication, because she was blamed for the abuse she received at the hands of the men. Being sewn up so tightly meant that sex would always be painful. Unsurprisingly, she hated sex. So knowing what I know and knowing just how many children are sexually abused, and how much more likely that abuse is when children are vulnerable through fragile family circumstances, my mind puts two and two together.

I'm not going to 'solve' all of Willow's problems. But I do think carefully about what I can do to help Willow feel better. I can at least help her not to feel so alone with regards to the allegation from Adrian and Susan.

I stand at the foot of the stairs. I can hear that she's in Lily's room mucking about. And that's good: nothing wrong with a little frivolity. I look for a copy of my first book, *Thrown Away Child* and open it at page 111. I head up to Lily's room and knock on the door with a smile, and a guaranteed pass: the currency of a family size bag of Maltesers in the other hand.

'Now, I know you are a little old for such things, but, my darlings, I'm going to read you a story,' I explain with a laugh.

Lily gives a little shrug and they both throw themselves on the bed, ready to listen.

I begin reading from my own book, without telling them what it is: *'One of my jobs was to take an old grey Hoover round the house and vacuum everywhere. I had to take it all the way upstairs, one step at a time, and then vacuum the whole house, top and bottom. This did mean that I could go into rooms I didn't usually go into – as I wasn't usually allowed anywhere other than my bedroom, the bathroom and the toilet and kitchen. This meant I actually went into Barbara's and Ian's bedroom.*

'Barbara and Ian are the foster parents,' I clarify, aware

that they are being plunged into a story they know nothing about.

'I had to hoover round the beds very carefully. I wasn't allowed to open any of the drawers in her tallboy or dressing table, which were all in matching dark wood. I also couldn't open the wardrobe: it was forbidden. It did mean I could hoover up any poo that had crumbled under the bed…

I break off again here to explain that the poo explanation was in the chapter before, part of a little practical joke played by the narrator, before continuing, *'and I always checked how things were going down there. I also had to polish the surfaces with Pledge and a yellow duster.*

'Barbara never wore make-up or perfume, and didn't have any jewellery like Maisie (bracelets, necklaces or beads).'

Again I stop to explain who Maisie was. Willow and Lily are busy munching through Maltesers, so it's difficult to gauge how much Willow, in particular, is taking it in. I resume reading aloud once more.

'But she did have a glass tree on her dressing table, which had three gold rings hanging on it. I polished the glass on the mirrors and the surface of the dressing table, and then I put my duster and the Pledge down. In my childish curiosity I slipped the rings onto my fingers and held my hand up to the mirror and put it against my face. Just like I had played with Maisie's rings. I stared at myself in the mirror and liked what I saw – three gold rings – and I wondered if they were her wedding and engagement rings.

'Just then the door flung open. There was Kevin.'

'Who is Kevin?'

'Kevin was the cock of the roost, older foster sibling of the family. He didn't get on very well with his younger foster sister.'

Lily nods sagely.

I continue, *'He saw me with the rings on my fingers. I jumped and put them back on the glass tree and felt very scared. Kevin disappeared as fast as he had appeared. I held my breath and listened. I could hear his footsteps going along the landing to his room. He wasn't going straight down to the kitchen to tell on me, so maybe it was alright. The threat of the police was still hanging over me. I didn't want to be whacked again with Barbara's Cuban-heeled shoes either. So I carried on dusting and Pledging and hoped everything would be alright.*

'Next morning, Sunday, I was waking up and Barbara shot into my bedroom, dragged me from the bed by my arm and pulled me to standing.

'"You little thief," she hissed. Ian was wandering along the landing in his pyjamas, and stood in the doorway. "Don't hurt her," he said meekly…'

I read the rest of the chapter and both girls look slightly shocked.

'Was that you, Louise?' Lily asks, quietly.

I smile. 'Yes, it was me. Barbara and Ian were my foster parents. And, while I was living with them, I was punished for something I did not do. There is nothing worse for a child, or anyone, actually. It's a horrible feeling.'

Willow looks thoughtful.

Later that evening when the children are getting ready for bed, I go to each room with Mabel, Lily's little tabby cat, to say goodnight. When I knock on Willow's door she is sitting up in bed with her arms laid out on her duvet. Her little bedside light is on. She lifts her head to look at me. Her face is pale and scared.

I take a step into the room. 'Are you okay, Willow?'

She chews on her lip. 'Can I talk to you Louise?'

Chapter Twenty-Four

Louise

Afterwards, I sit with Willow until she falls asleep. She likes to sleep with the curtains open. The night time lights from the town, the twinkling solar lights from the garden, and the moonlight through the window shine across her sweet, beautiful, innocent face.

I have tears flowing down my face onto my pyjama top. My neck and chest is soggy from crying. I could not hold back.

As Willow spoke, I cried.

I cried for the child. I cried for her past, and for her future. I cried for all the children who are hurt and abused by sick people.

She has spoken of surreal horrors tonight. She has told of systemic abuse which happened, not when she was in foster care, but before that, when she was living with her father. I don't know all the details, only what Willow has chosen to share. The abuse happened in their family home. It involved a group of men, over several years. These men were known to her father and they came to the house regularly. Her dad allowed the visits. Encouraged them, even, but wasn't present while the sexually-abusive acts were happening. The men chanted and prayed while they did unspeakable things to Willow. They wore masks and robes. They lit candles and performed 'acts of worship'.

I can't unsee or unthink what Willow has described. And it is horrible. Her descriptions of 'dirty, ugly men, dressed in costumes' who have 'dragged their disgusting penises' across her little body have made me feel utterly sick. Men, plural. Men who have put their fingers inside her body. A kind of ritualised abuse.

I'm saddened, and revolted. But perhaps not shocked. Since I discovered that my birth father was a serial paedophile and got away with it until he died, I am suspicious of everyone. Or should I reframe that as 'professionally curious'. Not a bad thing.

I wonder if Willow's father understood, on any level, what was happening to his daughter. Surely not. There was some connection between these men and the church, which would have given them some 'legitimacy', but from the sounds of it, I don't think these men she describes can be part of the church itself. It may be that they have used the church, somehow, to gain access to vulnerable parents like Jason. It sounds organised, systematic. And vile.

Willow is terribly conflicted about her father. He is not

one of the men who abused her, and at times she defends him. But the way she spoke at other times suggests that she blames him, at least in part, for not protecting her.

There is much more to get to the bottom of, but my hunch is that Jason didn't understand. I suspect he is even more vulnerable than the representatives from children's social care realise. I sit for a bit in the kindly lights, soothed by the sound of Willow's slow breathing, knowing that, at the very least, in telling me – unburdening herself by telling someone – she will feel a tiny, tiny bit better. At least that's what I hope.

I feel as though I'm reeling. In shock from hearing what she had to tell me. How much worse must it have been to go through it? Poor, poor Willow. And of course, it explains the pubic lice infestation in her eyes.

I sit there for I don't know how long. Eventually I rouse myself to go downstairs to a quiet house. The kitchen is dark. I walk through to the sink to get a glass of water. There is no need to turn on the light: I know my way around the space well enough and besides, the moonlight shows me the silhouettes of the chairs and the table.

The cold stone of the floor is reassuring under my bare feet. Until I feel something cold and wet under foot. I yelp, as my skin makes contact with something thick and slimy. Have I trodden on a slug? I walk back to the door and turn on the light, gasping as I realise that I have, in fact, stood in the intestines of a mostly-devoured mouse. It must have been brought in by Mabel.

I feel sick.

There is nothing for it but to hop to the kitchen roll in the corner, in between the microwave and the kettle. I wipe dark red blood and pieces of liver and heart from the bottom of my foot. Then I get out the anti-bac spray and spray my foot and the floor. While I'm doing all of this a horrible array of thoughts and images conjure themselves up in my mind. Most of which leave me thinking, 'Those dirty, fucking bastards'.

I decide that I need to sit and think about it all for a bit. I certainly can't go to bed with these thoughts in my head.

I have an urge to check on Willow once more. I trip up to her room and quietly open the door. She is sound asleep.

Back in the kitchen I go to get a bottle of wine from the wine rack. My eye wanders across the bottles standing upright next to it. Though they are in the kitchen, I never really take any notice but now I spot a bottle of port, left over from Christmas. I get a wine glass and fill it almost to the brim. I decide to go outside. It's chilly, so I grab two garden blankets from the box by the back door. I am still barefoot and hope I don't stand in anything else unpleasant. I *think* I picked-up all the dog poo today. I settle myself down in the firepit area where we have dinner and barbecues in the summer on the occasions when the sun does shine and it's warm enough.

I pull out two chairs: one for me and one for my feet. I put one blanket around me and the other across my legs and toes. I hold my giant portion of port and stare into the middle distance. I look up to the house, specifically to Willow's window. What a life that girl has had. And how long she has kept it all bottled up – not telling *anyone*. I just hope she is better for speaking out, and trust that we can now find a way forward for her. I try to organise my thoughts from the pragmatic details: the process of reporting this and what that will mean to Willow, and balance this with thinking about the sheer emotional weight of it on her tender heart – and my own. Perhaps the answer will lie at the bottom of the glass of port.

I drink!

Chapter Twenty-Five

Louise

In the morning I realise that the house is already busy and that I must have forgotten to set my alarm. I wake up, slightly disoriented, in the guest room – remembering that I didn't want to wake up Lloyd or breathe port-breath over him all night.

I remember that I also wanted to be alone.

I, too, was abused as a child – but not so brutally bizarrely as the account I heard last night. I need to focus my thinking once more, which is hard because I have a hangover. My head feels terrible. I realise that I have slept in, but it's Saturday morning so it doesn't matter that I missed making the children breakfast.

I hear all the children in the kitchen. Jackson and Lily have taken over and microwaved readymade pancakes. They've smeared chocolate, Biscoff spread and peanut butter on them, with strawberries and blueberries as a somewhat tokenistic nod to health.

I look towards Willow, wondering how she will be this morning after last night's intense disclosures. She seems fine, shovelling in her pancake and a hot chocolate. I say nothing as I head towards the top drawer of the cans cupboard and pull out a box of paracetamol. I know that I should not take tablets on an empty stomach. I notice half a pancake discarded on a plate near the kettle. It calls to me. I don't care who's watching, but the reality is no one is. They're too busy loading up on sugar and carbs. I eat the pancake and make a black coffee. Then I swig back some water to help down the two paracetamol.

I pull out a chair at the far end of the table away from all the pancake action and watch the children, unified by the sheer joy of eating what they started without me. They are smugly defiant. My window of opportunity to tell them how unhealthy that menu is has passed, and they, frankly, do not care what I think. And, honestly, today I couldn't give a hoot.

I glance at Willow again. She smiles. There is no attempt to avoid eye-contact with me. I find it hard to believe that she is this relaxed and in control. There is a chilled, Saturday morning vibe. Perhaps it's because all that sugar hasn't kicked in yet.

I hope no one is sick.

I'm truly grateful that it is the weekend. It gives me some time to process all I now know. I need to find Lloyd and share the news. It will rock his world. He gets despairingly upset at any kind of child exploitation and finds it really difficult to deal with. It's the injustice he can't cope with; the exploitation of innocence.

The headache is subsiding so I look for Lloyd. He's in the last place I expect him to be on a weekend morning: I eventually discover him in his office, working!

'You do realise it's Saturday,' I say as I walk in.

He laughs. 'There is no rest for the wicked.'

How lightly we use words like 'wicked' in everyday speech.

As I tell Lloyd about Willow's disclosures, his face pales and his eyes are heavy.

He lets out a deep sigh. 'Poor, poor Willow.'

I find that I have tears flowing in a steady stream down my face once more. I thought I had cried them all away last night. I scratch the back of my head and find a bit of twig. It must be from my nocturnal session in the garden.

'I'll write up a full report for Rupert and Moira tomorrow. There's nothing they can do until Monday anyway.' I feel weary about all that side of it. Rupert is young and has already ground my gears with his arrogance. Moira is a better ally, but she is leaving in a week. I can't face thinking about starting this whole story again with *another* supervising social worker. For now I just want to let this horror show settle.

'Those bloody men,' Lloyd growls. 'I'd love to get my hands on them!'

I check in on Willow a lot throughout the day. I am worried about her, as well as being sad beyond belief.

At lunchtime I go into Lily and Willow to see if they'd like to go out for a hamburger. Not the healthiest option after the sugar-fest for breakfast, but never mind.

'Do I ever!' Lily does her 'hungry dog' impersonation, tongue lolling while she pants, which always makes me laugh. I wonder if she will grow out of it. Willow looks up and something catches my eye beneath her chin.

'What's that on your neck?'

She moves her head down so that I can't see and makes a deadpan face. I'll have to wait and catch her off guard.

'McDonald's for you, too, Willow?'

She gathers herself up and pulls the sleeves of her inside T-shirt down over her hands, ready for action.

'Let's go!' I grab my car keys and usher the girls towards the back gate.

From the top window I hear a shout. 'Where are you going?'

Lily calls up, 'McDonald's!'

'Not without me, you don't,' Vincent calls back. 'Wait up!'

He pulls down the sash window and runs down the stairs holding his trainers.

'Any more?'

Jackson stands by the back door with his hand on his tummy. 'Can you bring me back a meal deal, please?'

Once in the car, I line up my mirror to try to catch a glimpse of Willow's neck. I don't have to be so discreet, it turns out.

Vincent pipes up. 'Why have you got a big cut on your neck?'

Willow shrugs her shoulders. I say nothing.

'So, gang, do we want to eat in or drive through?'

They all want the drive through. I pull up by the speaking machine and the young voice asks me if I'm using the app. I smile at this. I have a teeny group of apps on my phone and McDonald's is not one of them.

'No, I shall not be using the app. I'm paying by card.'

I can feel the embarrassment emanate from my passengers. 'Why should it matter to you how I order? You aren't paying, so just shush yourself and enjoy. Right, what's everyone having?'

I turn around to hear their orders, which I instantly forget and have to double check. I find myself apologising repeatedly to the young person in the machine.

'What drink?' I yell with some frustration, accidentally into the microphone rather than into the back of the car. 'Sorry, I need to let you know what drinks… just give me a moment.'

This particular drive through hardly ever has the flurries or milkshakes, but today there is partial success: one milkshake is available, but only one.

Hooray, and also boo, because that's not easily divided. No matter. 'Willow, that's yours,' I say, firmly.

Lily shoots me a murderous look. I will explain this to her one day, but right now, after what I know Willow has experienced, she can have whatever she wants. She has been systematically abused in her own home and has kept all of that bottled up inside. Milkshake is hardly going to register on her Richter scale of hurt, but it is the only thing I can do.

They munch away in the car quite happily for most of the way home. By the time we return, the feast has been demolished.

'Right, you lot, gather up your rubbish!'

The car stinks, but hey.

For some reason, the child lock is on and I can't seem to turn it off. I get out of the car and open Willow's door so that she can get out. Clutching her brown paper bag with all its debris, she forgets to hide her neck. I can see several cuts across it. Not scratches, cuts.

The fast-food-satisfied clan go into the sitting room to play Mario Kart and I go up to Willow's room to do a sweep for sharp objects.

At first I can't see anything, then as I look harder, I notice a small bump under her pillow. Beneath the fitted sheet is a razor blade. In her bin there are squares of blood-stained toilet roll.

The first time I found this the dots were little and sparse, a bit like when dads cut themselves shaving and stick tissue on their nicks. This is much more. There has been a clear escalation. This is getting serious.

I wonder when she did it. It must have been yesterday evening or this morning because the bloodied tissue wasn't there when I went round the rooms in the morning. Was it before or after our conversation?

I feel devastated all over again. I want to give her a hug. I go back downstairs and, with a cheerful, sing-song voice to disguise my true feelings, ask, 'Can I just borrow you, Willow, for a minute?'

We go into the kitchen and I show her what I have found. She puts her head down. I put my hand on her shoulder and, as she scratches and moves her T-shirt with her fingers, I notice more cuts, some new, some healing. I pull her in towards me and swamp her with a huge hug. She is crying. I am crying. I say, over and over again, 'Willow I am so sorry. I am so sorry for all that has happened to you.'

She pulls back a little and I look at her hot, damp little face. I sweep her hair up out of her eyes and away from her face. I smile at her, though my eyes are still wet with tears. 'It's going to be okay. It really is. But, my darling, we are going to have to report those men.'

She nods.

'I'm so proud of you for telling me what they did. But I've got to do something about it now. You understand that, don't you?'

She nods again and swallows.

'I did tell someone else.'

'What?'

226

She looks down to the floor.

'Who, Willow? Did you tell your father?'

She shakes her head.

I wait.

Through the shuddering sobs that still wrack her body, she tells me that she told her previous foster carers.

What? She told Adrian and Susan? There's no mention of that in her file. How could they have known this and not done anything about it? Adrian is the director of a fostering agency. What was he thinking?

This makes everything so much worse. It's not just the utter hideousness of the disclosure. But that this is not the first time she has told an adult what happened to her.

And yet nothing has been done about it.

And then I realise.

The allegation.

The men responsible would have been connected with their church, at least indirectly. They were protecting the reputation of their church. I can't believe how hypocritical that is.

'Is that when they made the allegation about the jewellery?'

Another nod. 'The next day.'

Jesus Christ.

What a sorry old mess this is.

But I need to be honest with Willow. 'I will have to tell Rupert that you have been cutting.'

She draws her lips into a tight round 'o' shape, then blows a big breath out through them and nods.

Lloyd works a double shift trying to keep everything normal. He does some DIY jobs around the house and garden, something he does most weekends. He whistles cheerfully while he works. I like it when he does this. I prefer the simple DIY fixes to his other favourite weekend pastime: busybody 'rationalisation' of various areas. This usually involves him going into a cupboard or drawers, dispensing with anything he decides is superfluous and reorganising systems that weren't in need of reorganisation.

In a recent rationalisation project he moved my little garden tools from where they have lived perfectly happily by the back door, down into the shed furthest away from the house. When I need to use the secateurs (frequently at this time of year), I have to go all the way down to said shed. By which point I've probably forgotten whatever quick job it was I was planning on using them for. It didn't take me long to smuggle them back to their more practical location. Every single time he takes it into his head to do this, none of us can find anything for days. Over time, often not that long, actually, as was the case with the secateurs, we all go back to our old ways. The greatest irony of all this is that most of the 'mess' in the house is actually Lloyd's! Once some small fixes and installations have taken place, which requires a quick trip to B&Q for some bits and bobs, he launches into the cooking, making a lovely Mexican feast for dinner.

After years of me slavishly making Sunday roasts week in, week out, the children collectively announced that they didn't, in fact, like roast dinner. It came as news to me, but since I was the one who made it every Sunday, I did not argue when Lloyd took over with his 'world food' approach to Sunday dinner. I decided that it wasn't worth being offended over and embraced the release it offered. You have no idea how much praise I pour on Lloyd for his cooking, all made with love. I'm not stupid. It's paid off. I'm the one who walks into *his* office at 6pm in the evening to ask, 'What's for dinner?'

Following our sumptuous Mexican repast, I take Willow to one side to ask if she has any more blades in her room – to which she shakes her head. She lies on her bed, scrolling through her phone.

'Do you want the door open?' I ask, in a tone that strongly suggests she should keep the door open.

She shrugs.

The boys are gaming with each other from their rooms and Lily is in her room, chatting on her phone to Sophie, her old friend, about Liam, a boy who I *think* Lily likes but Sophie is going out with. Drama!

Throughout the day I work on the reports for Rupert and Moira. I have thought carefully about the best way to organise the report, deciding to break it into three distinct sections.

The first section is a version of Friday evening and how it played out. What Willow revealed (minus the bits about me standing on mouse entrails and drinking so much port I couldn't remember arguing with a shrub in the garden until I pulled bits of plant detritus from my hair in the morning).

Section 2 is about the blades and cutting, the way that this has come to light and perhaps may have escalated since the disclosure.

The last section includes my research, my thoughts and my recommendations – which I have a feeling will be totally ignored, but nevertheless I try. My recommendations are, as always, aiming for a drip-drip, softly-softly approach. Let's not scare the horses is always my motto. Willow is a gentle, soft soul and I know that we need to tread very carefully. If there are heavy, 'blue flashing lights' interventions, she will regret telling me. I think it will set her completely off balance and make her life worse. If that happens then it will make her need to cut herself far worse, too.

I run the draft report by Lloyd to get a second opinion. He agrees with everything I've said. Years ago, when we started our fostering journey, Lloyd was paranoid that my honesty and tell-it-as-it-is approach to life would cause trouble. He was right, at times it did, but the trouble would have happened anyway and, over time he has become braver. Lloyd's father was a bully. He continually belittled Lloyd as a child, and as a man. When I met my father-in-law, I told him straight what I thought of him and, weirdly perhaps, he didn't seem to mind. In fact, he had a huge respect for my honesty. Frankly, I do not care what others think of me and it's a freedom and liberty that over time Lloyd has learnt, too. I find that 'middle finger' works, even if it's only in your head that you're using it.

With my reports approved, at least internally in the Allen household, I schedule them to send first thing Monday morning. I will also text Rupert and Moira to make sure that they are looking out for it. The local authority spent a fortune on a new system with a security firewall. Great in theory. In practice, it means that which emails and attachments actually make it through is pretty hit and miss. (Once we realised that they, and we for that matter, were not always receiving emails, I have found occasional opportunities to use that to my advantage. Confession over.)

Before I know it, the day has passed. Just before I go to bed I do my 'doctor's round' with Mabel the cat. I gently knock and peek around all their doors. A variation of 'You okay? Have you got everything ready for school?' They all say 'yes', but I know that won't be the case come tomorrow morning.

When I go in to see Willow, I sit at the end of her bed for a moment. She has the smallest room and her chair is covered in rock T-shirts and a guitar. The relentless tidiness has begun to slip. It must mean that she feels more at home. 'Are you alright, my beautiful flower?'

She smiles. I always call her 'beautiful' and I mean that she is beautiful inside. Since learning her story, I can't help but feel she is more beautiful than ever. 'I've written up the report,' I tell her, and give a sketch account of the contents. I try to reassure her that, 'It's all going to be okay,' and remind her that she is, 'one of the bravest girls I know.' I stay for a bit longer than with the others, talking a load of old blather and nonsense, but I sense that she enjoys me being there.

'I'm going to ask you again, and I'm sorry to do this, but do you have any blades or other sharp materials that could hurt you?'

'No.'

I look her straight in the eye.

'Are you sure?'

'No, Louise. I promise.'

'Can I ask you where you *did* get the blade from?' I'm slightly at a loss, because Lloyd uses a safety razor.

'I got them from Adrian. When I still lived there.'

'When did you start cutting?'

She looks away. 'When I was nine years old.'

She pushes the duvet forward and pulls up her T-shirt to reveal hundreds of small scars. Some are fresher. I look carefully. There are layer upon layer of cuts. Thin white lines criss crossing over each other, some rising in small mounds of thicker scars. Everywhere she could reach, her whole torso, the tops of her arms and legs. I never noticed before. I have never seen her body.

Little '#MeToo's carved into her flesh.

Chapter Twenty-Six

Louise

I thought I was on my way to bed, but I'm not ready to sleep. I head into the kitchen, not thinking about anything in particular. But, like watching carousel horses going around and around, I imagine the men who have abused Willow. I give them faces. I wonder about their families. They must have families.

I wonder about Willow's cutting. There are misconceptions about teenagers self-harming. It is more common than those unaffected might think. Self-harm hospital admissions for children aged eight to 17 in the UK jumped 22% in 2023, according to BBC reports. Most teenagers who engage in self-injury, like Willow, attempt to hide their injuries, choosing areas most often covered by clothing. Contrary to what you might think, the majority of teens are not looking for attention when they self-harm. Instead, they do it to make themselves feel better, to give them relief from emotional distress. Sadly, we've witnessed it several times now with different children who have been in our care.

I've never cut. I pulled my hair out when I was a child. It happened when, for a short time, I had two mothers living under the same roof, both my adoptive *and* birth mothers. It was an unusual, and emotionally complex time. I pulled my eyelashes first, then my arm hair, then the hair on my head. Since then, I've thought a lot about why. I did it, I think, because I was 'muted' by their double-presence. I had to think so carefully before I spoke, arranging all my sentences to avoid saying 'mum' to either of them, because I didn't want to hurt the other's feelings.

Children are kind; children want to protect their adults. On all sorts of levels. The burden should be the other way round, falling on the parent to protect the child, but that's not always the reality. I didn't think *why the hell am I sharing my home with two mothers?* I just found a physical way to react to the impossibility of it all.

Eventually, as the hairpulling escalated, it was inevitable that I would begin to resemble a bald frog. I remember the way that both of them peered at me with frowns.

'She's disturbed!' was the conclusion.

Well, no shit, Sherlock!

So, although I have never cut myself deliberately, I think I do understand a little of the compulsion to self-injury. If I think about Willow, living with a dad with learning needs, that's a scenario that's difficult enough for a young person to deal with. If that adult is then exploited by a group of manipulative, freaky, weirdo paedophiles, in order to get to Willow as she has described, that's horrendous. It's clear that she would have had nowhere to turn. She and her father were carefully isolated by them. No wonder she struggled to manage all those confusing feelings. At nine years old! It's heartbreaking. Absolutely heartbreaking. And sickening. And now to be reliving all that trauma.

That child has been totally failed by the adults around her.

I keep recalling the memory of when we went into the music shop in Bristol and how she played rock guitar. How she lit up when we bought her the Motorhead and ACDC T-shirts. How easy it is for her to be happy in spite of everything that has happened to her. I'm so glad she is able to find comfort and solace in her music. She is a beautiful soul who does not deserve to have been so ill-treated.

By Monday morning the email and the texts are sent. By the time I have walked from my studio back into the kitchen to put the coffee machine on, my phone rings. It's Moira.

'Hi Louise, you've had a busy weekend.'

'Yes, yes I have.' I leave the late-night large-port episode out of the conversation. A social worker is never your friend, and that is a fatal mistake that so many foster carers have made. I let out a deep sigh and then hear myself say, 'Fucking dirty old perverts!'

I know I should be more professional, but frankly, I'm

sick of it. Lily can't walk home from town without some old git calling her a prostitute; Marilyn, another child who stayed with us recently, was abused. Her mum was abused. The litany of others: Stella, Abby, Eden, poor little Jacob and Billy – God, his case still sends shivers down my spine. It's endless. I don't know what the answer is.

I honestly think that pornography has so much to do with what feels to me like an escalation of abuse in recent years. Perhaps it is exacerbated by the fact that porn can be accessed all day and night. I'm convinced that has contributed massively to the problem. My mind is filled with sick images of all those individuals watching porn, nursing hard-ons. How is it that *children* come to be on the receiving end of their sick satisfaction?

It's just as well I'm not a politician, because I would definitely not win many votes for the kind of measures I'd want to enforce in child exploitation and abuse cases. Testosterone suppression? Castration? Penis removal doesn't sound excessively draconian to me!

Anything that reduces the sexual desire that seems to turn some men into monsters would do. Maybe then the porn industry itself would shrink. Maybe men would start watching more gardening and cookery programmes. Oh, my, we live in a messed up world which makes looking after and protecting children such a big and important job for those of us who see the world for what it is and want to help children like Willow.

I've looked after a number of children whose stories are shocking, but Willow's, I think, feels so tragic – not least because she has borne so much and yet she holds herself with so much dignity. Every one of those cuts on her body reveals that she is suffering, but also that she is soothing herself.

No one was there to comfort her, no one held her and rocked her, no one wiped her tears away. That poor, poor child will now be re-traumatised as the police and the care professionals ask her tonnes of questions. My brain kicks into gear. I know that the police will want to question Willow too, because of the criminal prosecution side of things. They will also want to ensure that other professionals do not ask leading questions first. I know what I have to do. I'm thinking all of this whilst Moira is talking; I have no idea what about. I realise that I have totally tuned out of her conversation.

'Sorry, Moira, what did you say?'

'Oh, did the signal cut out?'

Well, my internal one did, just for a moment, but I don't tell her that. 'Not sure what happened. But I lost you there for a moment.'

'I was just saying that I'm due to talk to Rupert in the afternoon and then straight after that we'll have a professionals' meeting.'

'Are we part of the professionals meeting?' I ask, though I suspect I already know the answer.

'No,' she begins to say, and then stops, perhaps as she realises how that sounds. She will be perfectly aware of what foster carers think about 'professionals' meeting without the foster carers. Why can they not accept that the foster carers have more insight into what's happening with a child than the professionals? No doubt there will be people at this 'professionals' meeting who have never met Willow. Maybe they haven't even heard of her yet, will hear her name for the first time today, or are only just reading her case notes. Her situation will be all new news to them but old news for Willow, who has been living with this horror for several years, unsupported and unheard. So often we are left out of essential conversations about our children. It isn't surprising, then, that some foster carers do not consider themselves to be professionals.

'But I will, of course, keep you fully informed as to what outcomes are decided.' As Moira is talking she slows down the last few words, evidently distracted. I can tell she's reading something on her screen. She's at home. I can hear her dog barking in the background. She got a Cockapoo not that long ago, called Bernard. She comes back to me, 'Right, sorry, bit of an update. Rupert has asked you to keep her home from school tomorrow. He has spoken to the child protection team who want to come and interview her.'

I remember the lovely police woman who came to visit us when we looked after little Stella, a few years ago now. I tune back out from Moira's conversation. 'Right. Can you put all that in an email, please? I've got to go. Thanks, Moira.'

I call the police.

I'm put on hold and transferred a couple of times, but it doesn't take too long before I speak to a man who asks how he can help. I say, 'I am a foster carer of a young teenage girl who has recently made a serious disclosure.'

'Right—'

'It's very serious,' I repeat. I start to tell him what I know and he interrupts me.

'Have you reported this to children's social care?'

'Yes, I have. Which is exactly why I am calling you now. They want to visit Willow tomorrow, but I'm concerned that she will now be subjected to a long series of different adults asking her many probing questions about her past. I think that would be very dangerous. She does a lot of self-injury. She cuts herself. She has scars and cuts all over her torso, which I have only just seen.'

He is understanding and reassuring, just as I hoped he would be.

'Do you think you can prepare Willow to receive a visit from a couple of our experienced and trained officers this afternoon? That way we can prevent other professionals from speaking to her about the disclosures.'

Lloyd is out when I get off the phone, having popped to the shops with the expectation that today is going to be a long day – and we will therefore need supplies. Meal deals, in case the children can't come downstairs because people are here, and packets of biscuits, sweets, crisps and fizzy drinks. All the bad stuff that will help them stay out of the way.

When he returns, I explain to him what I have done in terms of bringing in the police first.

He frowns, and lets out a low whistle. For a moment I think he's going to be critical of the decision I've made. He computes the information and perhaps, like me, is trawling back to our experiences with young Stella when we worked with that supportive and effective policewoman.

He nods. 'Good idea!'

It's Action Stations here in the Allen household.

I put the coffee on and help to put the shopping away while planning what I'm going to say to Rupert and Moira about the fact that I've gone to the police. I am a big baby, and decide to get the police to deal with them. Moira is going anyway and Rupert is still wet behind the ears, so it'll be better that way.

The phone rings. It's a female police officer who arranges to be here at 4.30pm. That's great, because it will just about give me enough time to give Willow a drink and a snack before they arrive.

I hope she is having a good day at school.

A thought which reminds me to call the school and update them. I speak to the head, who I like very much, based on our few interactions so far. I still think he's too young to be a headteacher, but he gives every appearance of being all about the children, which is the right attitude in my book. I explain to him that Willow has made a number of disclosures and that the police will be here soon after she gets home.

'So I don't know if she will be coming in tomorrow. I'll let you know, of course, but it depends very much on how the police interview goes and how she feels afterwards. School and routine might be the best thing for her; equally, she might need some downtime at home.'

'Absolutely,' Mr Young replies. 'You are best placed to judge that.'

Yes, yes, I am, I think. What a contrast with the attitude of Rupert and Moira, excluding me from the discussion and decision-making entirely.

God, it feels tense. Lloyd is as edgy as I am. He can't settle down to anything. Neither can I. Even though all the children are at school, little actual work gets done by either of us.

When the other children arrive home, I try not to be too dramatic about what lies ahead. That's not easy to pull off. It's difficult to make, 'Darlings, two police officers are coming in an hour or so to talk to Willow' *not* sound dramatic.

They are goggle-eyed and full of questions, but I tell them I don't know the answers and bundle them off to their rooms with armfuls of supplies. I won't see them for a few hours.

When Willow comes to the door, I see that the clouds are gathering. I can feel rain brewing: that rain from hell that we seem to be getting more and more of. It's like monsoon rain but without the sunshine at the end. I make a mental note to ask Lloyd to put the flood gate up once the police have arrived. I can hear seagulls circling. We are a good 20 minute drive from the nearest beach, but they do this when the weather turns bad.

A sudden screech from a gull makes me jump. I am so on edge.

I hope we are not going to make things worse for Willow, by taking the course of action I've chosen. It is out of my hands now. It literally depends on who is sitting in front of her, and how they manage the difficult conversations that will inevitably ensue.

Outside, it begins to rain. Great, thick splatters cover the windows. The rain from hell. I hope Willow's taxi isn't too far away. The last thing we need is for her to be stuck because of the next village being flooded and cars not being able to get through. Once again, I lament the decisions that have been made locally. If only we could blame 'climate change', a phrase that seems to have become a byword for 'let's not bother to do anything'. What's happening in our area has nothing to do with the climate crisis and everything to do with mismanagement of the infrastructures, such as drains and land. If we keep laying concrete and tarmac where do they think the rainwater is going to go?

It strikes me that this, too, feels like a metaphor for what has happened to Willow and explains her cutting. If her abuse is not dealt with, where are those feelings going to go?

They go into her flesh.

I walk backwards and forwards to the kitchen, feeling as

though I'm going to wear a trench into the stone floor with the continued pacing.

Not a peep from the other children; they are clearly occupied, and following their instructions to stay out of the way.

Lloyd begins setting up the flood gate just as the taxi pulls in. Willow's little face is staring at her phone. I dash off a text as quickly as I can. *Hello darling, look up.*

She does, and sees me waving. She smiles.

I stand in the doorway as she comes in. 'How are you? How did your day go?'

'Alright.' Standard teenage response.

'Can you come into the kitchen for a moment? I need to talk to you.'

Don't we all hate that? 'I need to talk to you' is rarely the opening line of something good.

'Sandwich?' I ask, already spreading the peanut butter and jam onto bread. It's her current favourite.

'Are you alright, Louise?'

Bless her. I explain, as gently as I can, that two 'really nice' policewomen are coming over to chat to her about what she told me the other day. I hope this is true and that they are nice. 'They want to talk to you about those men.'

She inhales sharply.

'Those disgusting, vile men, who hurt you. Trust me, Willow, you did nothing wrong.'

She takes a bite from a sandwich and nods.

After her snack I suggest she goes upstairs to change, which she does. I have already made the sitting room a safe, quiet space for them to talk.

The door knocker goes a few minutes later and the dogs start barking. To my relief the police officers are not in uniform. The dark, imposing attire, designed for authority, is always horrendous for children – unless there has been a murder or robbery; then kids are fascinated by the batons and tasers and radios. I welcome the officers into the hall, apologising as they navigate their way over the flood gate. They introduce themselves as Sally and Shivani. We chat briefly about flooding and agree about how bad it is. They then follow me through to the kitchen. The dogs are sniffing their legs and wagging their tails.

One of them laughs. 'They must be able to smell Arlo, my dog!'

I offer teas and coffees which they welcome.

'Willow will be down in a minute. She's just upstairs getting changed. She's obviously expecting you and I've let her know you're here.' I confess that I'm stressed about this interview because I'm worried for Willow. They are kind and smile.

They both seem nice and have already put me at ease. Or at least as at ease as I can be, under the circumstances.

Lloyd comes in to greet the police officers, followed by Willow who, it comes as no surprise to me, is clad in a Motorhead T-shirt. I've managed to solve the problem of washing it while it appears to be spot-welded to her body by buying her multiple variations. This is her third Motorhead T-shirt. I found a specialist website, so her rock band T-shirt numbers have increased dramatically.

'Hi there, you must be Willow,' says Shivani.

Sally smiles. 'Great T-shirt. I'm a big rock fan myself. Who are your bands?'

Willow brightens and lists off all her favourites, which takes a while.

Shivani says, 'I'm more of a fan of hip hop myself, but Sally and I can still work together – just about,' and laughs.

They are creating just the right atmosphere. I like these two, and I can see that Willow does, too. I put their drinks on, along with a hot chocolate for Willow and, because I have decided that I like them, the treat of a plate of biscuits.

'Follow me,' I say, leading them to the sitting room. I settle them down and 'ask' the dogs to go. They obey; reluctantly, it has to be said, with a cock of the head to one side, as if to say, 'Really?' followed by their best 'hmmmphhh' expressions. Dotty lies down by the door on the other side with her head resting on her front paws. Doug follows me back to the kitchen in the eternal hope that I will drop a biscuit on the floor.

We've already agreed that Willow will be interviewed without me present. While a parent or guardian is generally required to be there when someone of Willow's age is interviewed by the police, there are exceptions, such as now, when the nature of Willow's disclosure means that too many adults in the room might be overwhelming. The overarching principle is always the protection and safeguarding of the minor's rights and welfare. Shivani explains that she will conduct the interview, and that Willow can call for me if she wants.

I go to my studio to try to do some work. Perhaps I can settle into something now that the police are actually here.

There is an email from Rupert with a couple of forms attached for us to fill out before the child protection social worker comes tomorrow. I email back and say, *Thank you, Rupert.* I am not thankful in the slightest, but I'm attempting to ease the wheels of professional communication. As much as I confess to disliking Rupert, I am attempting to be grown-up. I'm perfectly aware that you don't have to like someone to work with them. But it definitely helps.

I'm also ever-so-slightly perturbed by the fact that I've effectively gone behind his back in taking Willow's case to the police. I'm effectively telling a little white lie in not mentioning the police visit to him. Being bold with him is slightly scary; not because *he* is scary, so much as whom he works for is. Children's social care departments can make life very difficult indeed. In our experience they have a reputation for throwing out allegations like hand grenades when the foster carers have displayed any hint of asserting themselves.

No, it's Rupert's manager and his manager's manager

that worry me. I don't even know who they are, but I know that they wield enough power to make life difficult for any foster carer who challenges them. I am thankful for the existence of the NUPFC (National Union of Professional Foster Carers). I know that they have my back. I have run scenarios by them several times over the years, as well as using Foster Wiki to find the correct legal position in some situations. Sometimes the law and government legislation is news to social workers; even their seniors can seem a little rusty on legal points and interpretation of policy.

So, I go back to my email and change, *Thank you, Rupert* to: *That's great, thank you Rupert. Just letting you know that the police are with Willow, now.*

There. Backs covered. He can stick that in his pipe and smoke it. Perhaps he'll move more quickly the next time he is confronted by such a serious disclosure.

The police end up spending over an hour in the sitting room. I knock on the door, interrupting with a resumption of my Mrs Overall from *Acorn Antiques* performance, and ask if anyone would like another drink, as if all problems can be solved with a nice cup of tea.

They all say yes. I try to gauge the atmosphere in the room, taking a surreptitious look at Willow's face. It tells me very little. She seems calm enough, but then she always does *seem* calm. But all those cuts on her body tell a different story. She's been very precise in her actions, and hasn't cut on her arms or legs, where the cuts could more easily be seen. It's as if she didn't want to be found. Some like to theorise that cutting is a cry for attention, but Willow hiding hers makes that argument sound a bit weak. I have certainly learnt that with Willow we don't know what's really going on. That in itself is unsettling since it means that I'm constantly worried that I'm misreading her. That there is something else running through her head and her heart, other than what I think I can see.

It is another hour after the second lot of drinks that the door eventually opens. I walk along the hall to greet the little party. I check Willow and try to decode her unreadable face.

She looks tired. I call Lloyd and ask him to make Willow a snack. That is today's code for 'keep her safe while I talk to the police'.

I smile at them both expectantly.

'Have you got a minute?' Shivani asks.

You bet.

We return to the sitting room and shut the door

Sally asks me what I know about the 'Moloc Group'.

I've never heard of it, and have no idea what they're talking about. 'Absolutely nothing,' is my honest response.

Sally begins to explain. 'Actually, I'm not surprised. They have actively avoided creating any kind of online presence because it enables them to keep off the radar, somewhat. I was working abroad a few years ago when I came across them for the first time. I think the choice of name is deliberate: there was a Moloch in the bible, different spelling but close enough to be plausibly connected. Some sort of a god of the Canaanites, so it lends them a ring of legitimacy. But they are anything but. There was an organised paedophile ring operating within the group. They had created a cell within a broader church group and used the church and the congregation as a way to reach, specifically, vulnerable adults who have children.'

Already I start to see how Jason – and therefore Willow – would fit this profile, given Jason's learning needs and their existing church connections.

'It's quite systematic. They start off by helping the family and, of course, the church with whom they are connected think it's great that additional support is being provided. Then, one of them will start to move in on the vulnerable adult, developing the relationship into a 'friendship' by going round to see them on their own in their home, and starting to get to know the child or children.'

Sally speaks more slowly as she says the next part.

'They spend time grooming the parents, who are usually single and almost always have learning issues. They are singled out. It all starts innocently enough. They'll knock on the door and introduce themselves as being from the local church. They befriend the target and show interest in the children, or child. They offer help and support, they invite them to the church to help grow the congregation and make them look good. They bring gifts for the children. As time goes on and the trust is established, they suggest a prayer room. The prayer room requires a black out blind, which they provide and, when in prayer the blind is always pulled. As time goes on, they bring in more members, who begin to perform rituals in the home, wearing costume. That makes it sound very sinister. Which it is. Think *Wicker Man*, and the villagers paying homage to pagan gods – including children as part of the 'celebrations'. Perhaps the costumes make it easier for them to stay in role, like actors, and to–,' here she pauses for a moment, 'well, to do what they do.'

She doesn't need to spell it out. I already feel sick. In our years of foster care we have encountered more cases of child sexual abuse than I can count. When that abuse is *organised*, it is even more horrific. Hearing that it is both organised and ritualistic, and that Jason has been targeted because of his learning needs feels utterly vile and wicked. Not that there should be gradations of this kind of horror. It makes me despair for the world.

Sally goes on to explain that the members of the particular group she encountered previously were all married and had their own children.

That makes me feel even more sick, somehow. It's worse than if they had not. More wicked, if that's possible.

'We don't know, yet, if that's exactly what's happened in Willow's case, but given what she has described, we are sensing a very similar pattern.'

I have so many questions, but I will wait for another day. Right now I need to focus on Willow.

'So, what's next?'

Shivani takes over now. 'We'll communicate with Willow's social worker and the school, so don't worry about that.'

I explain how I have already let Willow's social worker know that they were coming here today. I smile, ruefully. 'And I don't doubt that there will be repercussions for contacting you directly myself.'

Sally is reassuring. 'You absolutely did the right thing, no question.'

'We will speak to social services and manage the lines of communication. We can create an information centre for Willow that means that she does not have to keep being asked questions by different professionals,' Shivani says. 'As I'm sure you know, Louise, it can be too much for a child if they have to keep repeating their story. Sometimes they end up changing their truth as they feel pressured or, even worse, feel that they must please an adult's curiosity.'

I'm impressed by Shivani's words. That has to be just about the most intelligent and informed view I have come across to date.

'Yes, children say things to please an adult.' I did it so much as a child because we want to please everyone, it's safer. But in truth it just creates a mess. This is a much more humane approach. I see them out and walk into the kitchen where I discover Willow and Lloyd standing by the freezer. The door is open and they are busy selecting a Ben and Jerry's flavour for Willow.

I walk up to Willow and give her a huge hug. Then I tell her how brilliant she is and that she does not have to go to school tomorrow if she doesn't feel like it.

Willow does a little fist pump then turns back to the freezer to make her selection. 'Phish Food, please.'

Lloyd reaches to the top shelf and gets it for her.

I ask if she wants to come and watch a film with me.

'No film, but I'll come in if we can watch *Friday Night Dinner*!'

Why do the girls love the goofy stories of the Goodman family so much? I have no idea, especially when every episode of the show seems to follow such a similar routine and formula to the last one. But I'm not going to argue, especially if it makes them laugh.

We settle down on the sofa. I put my arm around her and pull her in tight. I can hear the clank of the spoon on her teeth as she enjoys the chocolate ice cream with gooey marshmallow and caramel swirls and, most importantly, fudge fish.

All is as well as it can be.

I do my very best to push away intrusive thoughts about what I've learned. How much harder must it have been for all these months for Willow to do the same?

Chapter Twenty-Seven

Louise

Willow tells me some of what she told Shivani and Sally.

The men who abused her wore white headdresses with a cord around them, like shepherds from a nativity play. One wore a set of horns on his head. The man in the horns also wore a pale bronze cloak made from cheap fabric. Sessions took place in the prayer room: a space that was once Willow's bedroom. She was barefoot and dressed in a white, 'old-fashioned nightie'. I picture an Edwardian gown. The men lit candles creating a kind of altar. The horned man spoke as if he was saying a prayer, like Willow had heard from church. It was confusing for her. They told her that she was a good girl. The men chanted: 'Willow is special; Willow is good.' She began to feel comfortable and even began to look forward to the prayer sessions because they gave her so much positive attention. As time went on and her misguided love for the men grew, they began to carry out their dark work. Ritualistic masturbation and touching her. When they had finished the 'purification', Jason would take her into the bathroom, shower her and put on her pyjamas. One by one the men would kiss her goodnight before they left and went back to their lives.

Over time, the abuse increased in its nastiness. Always ritualistic, the touching and masturbation became a kind of turn-taking gang rape. The whole thing revolts me.

It all goes quiet after the interview, for about a week. Then, on Thursday morning, out of the blue, I receive an official complaint from Rupert's manager, via the LADO (Local Authority Designated Officer). The complaint is centred around the fact that I have basically gone to the police without their permission, but it is framed as a complaint about my 'conduct and ability to keep 'W' safe because of your unsafe behaviour(s) around her.'

I think something in textspeak: *ffs*.

But it is laughable that they actually can't name anything specific that I have supposedly done.

This is sour grapes because I had the audacity to contact the police myself, before they got stuck into Willow.

It is of zero surprise; in fact, it simply confirms exactly what I suspected when I talked to Sally and Shivani. I knew this was coming.

But I mentally stick two fingers up to them. In the interim we have been to panel and have been approved for the new fostering agency I was looking into, Fostering UK. So, it does not matter what the local authority says, we're leaving in less than 28 days. If they want to make our lives difficult, I will call the union – the NUPFC – and let them deal with the authorities. I am past caring now, and loving the empowerment that realisation brings.

So, I take a small pleasure in not engaging with it at all. Instead I email Rupert, and copy in Moira.

> *Hi Rupert,*
>
> *I hope you are well? I'm just letting you know that we will do a daily log for Willow from here on in. I am concerned that she is cutting herself more and, thus far, I can't find the blades that she evidently brought with her from her previous placement. I think she has skilfully put them somewhere where I can't find them. I should also let you know that I have found more bloodied tissues in her room. Some have been carefully placed at the back of her drawers to avoid me easily discovering them. Additionally, her mood seems to have dropped.*
>
> *Best wishes, Louise.*

Moira emails straight back, again cc-ing Rupert for the records.

> *Thank you for the updates, Louise. They are very much appreciated.*

I take back everything I might have said about Moira. She has a good heart and has been broken down by the system just as much as we have. She spent half an hour on the phone with me yesterday basically bitching about all aspects of the way she has been forced to work. She also laid into Rupert, whom she calls the 'fledgling'. She told me over and over again how glad she is to be leaving. I echoed those sentiments.

It definitely feels like jumping from a sinking ship.

I have already made sure that I've also spoken to Fostering UK and have updated them with everything that's been going on. They are busy putting in plans to support Willow for when we move over to their jurisdiction. They are so helpful and genuinely seem to care about the best outcomes, which seems to have got lost in translation elsewhere.

They also received the reference from Rupert for us *before* he made the complaint, so that was good timing from our point of view.

Sally has been calling daily to check in and see how Willow is. She has also been really generous about sharing where they are in the investigation.

'We're in the process of gathering information and evidence about the Moloc Group. We've been to Jason's home and searched for the costumes that Willow described and, sure enough, we found them there in a sideboard cabinet, exactly where she said. I was trying to avoid it, but we may have to ask Willow some more questions,' she pauses on the phone. 'And it would be really helpful if she was able to look at some photographs of the six men whom our officers have questioned.'

My heart sinks. I wonder if looking at photos of her abusers might be too disturbing for Willow. It sounds like a straightforward thing to do, but it means reopening old wounds once more. I don't like the sound of it, especially as I am finding it so difficult to gauge Willow's feelings at the moment.

I say 'at the moment', but I realise that I've never been able to: not since the moment she first arrived with us, and that odd moment where she asked me if I believed in God and I dodged the question. Right now, I am so grateful if any of us can make her smile. The boys have tried to invite her to play Mario and other games but she's not keen. Never impolite, of course, just far more reluctant to engage with them than she was.

Lily comes into my studio.

'I don't want to tell tales.'

'But—?' I prompt, gently.

'But I think that Willow might be watching some quite scary stuff.'

'What sort of scary stuff?'

'Stuff about self-harming.'

'Okay. I'm glad you've told me, but how do you know?'

She shrugs.

'And how is she able to? You know that we have set up parental controls so that sort of stuff shouldn't be accessible.'

Lily laughs. 'They don't work. Everyone knows how to bypass parental controls.'

Well, this is depressing.

'She's going on Twitter and Tumblr,' she continues.

'It's really easy to find content on self-harming and eating disorders.' Lily shows me.

There are groups of people *encouraging* children to hurt themselves to cut. There are eating disorder groups that offer a buddy to help you starve yourself to death. WTF? Seriously? What is going on here? How is this allowed to happen? Who has responsibility for managing this kind of digital content? Why isn't it illegal? Or, if it is, why is nothing being done about it?

I am furious. I remind myself not to be cross with Lily; she is doing a good thing by showing me all of this. I'm enraged by the whole, nonsensical world that we are forced to live in. And frustrated that Willow's access to this is so out of my control. The anger and frustration is replaced by a kind of depression when I realise the futility of those emotions.

But I can't simply do nothing at all. It's a drop in the ocean, but I decide that, from now on, all the phones will be kept in our room overnight. No exceptions. There will be no sneaking down in the night to retrieve devices. I rue the day that Willow was allowed to have a bloody phone. I don't know what else to do. I have tried closer monitoring of the other children's phones in the past, tried to get passwords out of all of them, but as soon as I have looked at their phones they change the password and, when I ask to see their phones they delete everything that I'm looking for.

Lily shows me more and more pages of people cutting;

of people *filming* children doing it. Jesus Christ. I also see that it is mainly girls cutting. To me, it looks like the girls do not know that they are being filmed. Where the hell are they? Who is filming them?

There is more. There are videos of decapitation and graphic murders, all easily accessible. If Lily can find them, many other children will be watching. Clickbait links sometimes take the children to these videos when they aren't even looking for them. It feels like there is no escape.

This is a sick society that has been created from the invasive ubiquity of these bloody phones. I know I will be starting to sound like a stuck record, but when they wrote the Children Act in 1989, the authors absolutely must have been aware that the tech boom in the early 90s was just around the corner. It is a document that isn't fit for purpose. It *seriously* needs updating. Why hasn't someone done something about it? Where is the joined-up thinking on this so-serious issue?

It doesn't matter what the odd report says about screen time for gaming or social media having some positive effects, I challenge anyone to tell me that life for children has not become worse since every child in the western world has a phone and instant access to God knows what. It's just been proved to me by Lily that we haven't a clue about what they are watching. In what other circumstances would we expose our children to such an unknown environment without supervision? It's crazy.

I spend some time with Lily, getting her to screenshot

everything and send it to me. I plan to send it to the police, and Rupert and Moira, after I have checked on Willow.

The poor child has not been to school for a few days now. It is almost as if she is shrinking before our eyes. Physically, there is less and less of her, but she is dwindling away inside herself, too – or at least that's how it seems. I knew that there would be some kind of deep emotional consequence from Willow's disclosure, but this is serious.

Within half an hour of sending the images there is a reply from Sally. We are to take Willow immediately to the main police station where she and Shivani work.

Chapter Twenty-Eight

Louise

Willow shrugs when I tell her the news. Resigned to her fate.

I leave Lloyd at home with the others. He's got tonnes of work to do for a big exhibition coming up in India. He creates all the graphics. He doesn't go to these shows, which I know he would love to, but the miracles of modern technology(!) mean that we are able to watch the footage and he enjoys seeing the reactions of members of the public to his work. But it is time-consuming in the days leading up to the event. He waves me away with assurances that he is able to multitask quite effectively, thank you very much, and can manage to work and parent while we're gone.

Willow is quiet in the car.

I can see more and more cuts. She is no longer keeping the area of cutting to her torso. I can see them on her hands and arms. I can't ignore it, but I also can't judge her.

I just say, 'You've been cutting, Willow. Would you like me to get you a first aid box for your room?'

She nods.

This is not the same child who first arrived with us. I miss her. I miss hearing the music from her room. I miss her smile that revealed those large teeth that she will have to grow into.

What have those dirty old bastards done to this child?

'I'll sort that out for you when we get back from the police station.'

She nods again. She has been through so much in the last few days, and has talked so much about what happened to her. It seems now as if she is done talking. Perhaps there are no more words left.

The police station is on an industrial estate. We drive past a carpet warehouse and a trampoline play centre. There are lots of little vending vans selling sandwiches and drinks. It's a huge, sprawling complex of industrial buildings, and my sat nav appears to have sent me to an engineering firm. I can see the police station on the other side, so I drive back round and find the right road.

There is loads of parking available at the front of the building, and I also spy a massive multi-storey car park as I drive by, full of police cars and a row of big vans parked in a line. Beside it is what must be the staff car park, which is flooded with cars. I follow 'Visitors' signs and find that where the visitors go there is only one other car. It is occupied: the driver is sitting at his wheel eating a sandwich.

We go in through the main entrance doors. Immediately to one side is a row of booths where we can talk to a person.

I hold Willow's hand but she pulls away. I walk with her and say quietly, 'It will be okay. I'll stay with you.'

We stand in front of a woman who looks quite motherly. She's older than me and has a warm, friendly manner. She has a mic headphone set on and smiles through the protective screen. It's sad that protective glass is required on what is essentially a front reception, and it's a bit like what I imagine prison to be.

Prison. Prison is too good for those disgusting men to go.

We state our business and sit down. I watch a woman dragging a vacuum cleaner along the brush matting at the front. It's a bit early to be cleaning but hey ho. From the car park and sitting here alone with Willow, it looks like there are no crimes at all.

Sally soon appears through a nearby door, smiling and welcoming. Today she is wearing a uniform. That throws me slightly but, thankfully, Willow seems to have already decided that she likes her and doesn't seem bothered by it. We follow Sally through another set of locked doors that she gains entry to electronically, using her badge. We then enter a rabbit warren of white corridors and encounter some rather interesting-looking characters. I feel as if I'm on the set of some kind of intense television police drama and imagine them as teams of cold-case detectives and serial-killer investigators.

We go into a little room and Sally asks if Willow minds if we are joined by Carl, another detective working on the case.

Willow shrugs and shakes her head. 'I don't mind.'

Sally punches something into her mobile.

A couple of minutes later, in comes Carl. He is a pale-skinned, red-headed man in a suit, probably in his early forties. He wears a large, gold wedding band on his left hand wedding finger. When he smiles he seems friendly but he has one of those faces that when not smiley looks quite scary and stern.

I feel intimidated, so what the effect is on Willow, I can only imagine. Aware of my own childhood trauma still lingering, I tell myself to pull it together and shut up. I also have a little word with myself about not trying to make him smile, which is what I would have done to make myself feel safe, if I were in Willow's position.

I sit next to Willow and stay quiet while Carl and Sally talk us through what is going to happen.

'We'll look at some pictures of some men to see if Willow recognises them,' Sally explains.

I feel the tension as we all pull our chairs forward to their best viewing positions. The images are on a computer screen.

The first face is a bearded old man. Other than the beard, there doesn't seem to be anything particularly distinctive about him, initially. But Willow looks at him and says immediately, 'Yes, he's one of them.'

I look harder. What is it about him that makes him a paedophile? Is it his eyes, his mouth, his hair, his beard? I know that physiognomy is an outmoded Victorian pseudo-science, but it's human to link appearance with behaviour in our search for 'answers' to the unanswerable.

Up comes another face: a slim man with no beard this time. Younger than the first. He has thick, hedgehog-hair, with a widow's peak. It's going white in places.

Willow nods.

Then we move onto another face. An older man again. He has a big nose and a bald head. I look hard at his face. He's ugly and a bit creepy, that's for sure.

Willow nods once more and swallows. 'He was the one who always wore the horns.'

I take a deep breath in.

Carl notices and looks towards me in a sort of 'you okay there?' way.

I look back at Sally who tells Willow how well she is doing.

Next face, another old man, also balding, but with pronounced sideburns. He looks like an old farmer from a bygone age. Almost a caricature. But there is something shady-looking about him. I don't like his face. His horrible sneer. Or am I imagining it? It's horrible to do this. Impossible to do it in a detached way.

Willow shakes her head, and says, 'No'.

I'm almost disappointed. He definitely looks dodgy to me. I take another breath, this time much louder. I touch Willow's arm. 'Good girl, you're doing brilliantly.'

She makes a gentle movement with her mouth. There is nothing to say.

Up comes another face. A younger man, maybe in his mid-thirties. He looks plain, ordinary, nondescript. Something about the size of his face, or perhaps the angle from which the photograph has been taken makes me think that he must be short.

Willow nods.

Carl says, 'Thank you, Willow. You're doing a good job. Just a few more.'

I wonder how many of these sick creeps there are in this *Guess Who?* of paedophiles.

Up comes another face, a younger man again, with sticky out ears and longish hair arranged in a centre parting. He has dark, slightly-hooded eyes.

Willow nods.

'Just two more to go, Willow,' Sally says.

Next is a swarthier man. Short hair and glasses. He looks educated, somehow. Perhaps it's the glasses that make him look studious, or the way he seems to be peering at the camera inquisitively.

Another nod from Willow.

The last one appears; an old man, with neat silver hair. He looks *normal*, like a kind grandfather who would have set up a trust fund for all his grandchildren. I'd sit next to him on the bus. He looks gentle and harmless. He can't possibly be one of these freaky people.

But Willow nods.

I look at the desk and breathe out. It's over. I put my

hand back onto Willow's arm and give her a little squeeze. I say several times, 'Well done, Willow.'

But I can't get my head around this last man's face. He looks affluent. Incapable of hurting anyone. I can't explain it. He has a good haircut, he doesn't look like a drinker. He really does look like someone's nice grandad. In fact, he reminds me of Lloyd's mum's second husband, who passed away some years ago, and was a lovely man. He taught the boys to play chess, painted watercolours and enjoyed opera.

That's what old men should do!

What's wrong with these people?

Carl and Sally get up, pushing their chairs under the table.

'Thank you, Willow. I know that was tough,' Sally says. 'But you've done a really important thing here today.'

Carl echoes her, offering more effusive praise for the way Willow has conducted herself.

I pick up my bag from the floor, and that's that. We're done. All over.

Sally walks us out to the front reception area where she once again praises Willow as she holds the door open for us. 'We'll be in touch soon,' she promises, and smiles.

I shiver. What is there to smile about?

Chapter Twenty-Nine

Louise

Later that evening, I'm sitting downstairs, totally engrossed in another Scandi police drama when I receive a notification on my phone. It's a text from Willow.

Help me please.

Oh God. I dash straight upstairs to her room. There is a horrific mess. Willow is sitting on her bed, bent over her knees, with a towel across her legs, trying to stop blood that is pouring from her ankle.

I go into instant first aider mode: primary survey.

The cut is deep and near her bone. Beneath the gouged flap of skin there is tissue and gore and so much blood. I keep pressure on the towel each side of the cut while I kick the door open with my foot, and call Lloyd. 'Lloyd! Lloyd! Can I have some help here?'

Willow has fainted.

I keep calling Lloyd, but Jackson is nearer and comes in first.

'Shit!'

He runs out to the top of the stairs and calls, 'Dad, Dad, Daaaaaad!'

'Jackson! Here!' I call him back into the room. 'I know you've never done it before, but can you call for an ambulance?'

He begins nodding furiously but doesn't actually move to do anything.

'Do it. Quickly. Fetch your phone and dial 999 now!'

Lloyd walks towards the door, 'What's going on?' From the doorway he surveys the carnage. 'Oh my God! Is she alive?'

Jackson is back now, clutching the phone. He pushes past his father.

'Put it on speaker!'

The calm tone of the call handler comes over loud and clear. 'Hello, which emergency service do you require?'

'Ambulance.'

We are transferred. 'Hello, ambulance emergency. Tell me exactly what's happening?'

'I have a child who has self-harmed and cut through to her ankle bone. She has lost consciousness.'

Lloyd looks at her closely. 'And she's been sick.'

The call handler says, 'Has she taken anything? Any sign that it might be an overdose?'

I scan the room but can't see anything obvious.

Jackson opens her bedside table drawer and finds four empty packets of paracetamol. He holds them up. His face is grim.

I relay to the call handler what he has discovered.

'Are you able to put her into the recovery position?'

Lloyd acts quickly now and we work together to move her carefully into recovery. I'm grateful for the first-aid training I've received.

'Is she breathing?' the call handler asks.

I look at her chest and see it rise and fall. 'Yes! Yes! She is breathing!'

Thank goodness.

The call handler asks for my name and address. Jackson takes over the call while I keep my hand on the towel, now wrapped around her ankle and blood-soaked.

Lloyd is looking a bit pale. I give him something to do, suggesting that he goes to get some more towels. Vincent and Lily are looking on agog: horrified and obviously desperate to know what's going on.

'Vincent, put the dogs in their cages,' I command, anticipating the paramedics' arrival.

'Lily, go and fetch a glass of water.'

The water is for Lloyd, not for Willow, but everyone needs a job.

Lloyd returns from the airing cupboard with an assortment of towels, but he's clearly struggling. He needs to step outside the room once more. 'Lloyd, you wait outside for the ambulance. Make sure there's somewhere they can stop.'

Of course there's somewhere they can stop. I just need him out of the way.

Lily comes in with a glass of water for Lloyd but he's already left. 'Go and take it to Lloyd outside.'

She goes off to find him.

Vincent is back from rounding up the dogs. 'Talk to Willow,' I say.

'What about?'

'Anything you can think of.'

The call handler says that the ambulance is nearly with us and that she will stay on the line until they arrive.

Vincent is gabbling away to Willow in language I don't understand: Frappe Snowland, Choco Mountain. Donut Plains. I wonder why he's picked food as a subject and then realise it's something to do with Mario Kart. Good lad. He's doing a grand performance, worthy of a round on *Just A Minute*.

I keep a constant eye on Willow's breathing. Flutters of panic if I think I can't detect breath, but she is definitely still with us.

Vincent runs out of steam and reaches over to the borrowed CD player which has one of Lloyd's old CDs in it: *Ten* by Pearl Jam.

He holds it up and I nod.

He puts it on and turns it up. The call handler says, 'Are you having a party?'

'No, no. My other child has put Willow's music on to comfort her.'

Vincent points at the uninjured foot, moving.

'It seems to be working,' I add.

No sirens, but the room begins blinking blue with the arrival of the emergency vehicle. I hear conversations below, and people and kerfuffle, and then fast footsteps up the stairs. The paramedics come in and check her over. They take over from me and I can go and wash the blood off my hands. When I return I go through everything that's happened with the paramedics. They decide that she needs to be taken to hospital straight away, so fetch the stretcher. Everything happens smoothly and efficiently. We watch Willow stretchered into the ambulance, still unconscious.

'Can I come too?' I ask. I don't want to leave her.

'Yes.'

I grab my bag and get in the ambulance as well. Lloyd runs out and hands me my mobile.

'Will you call EDT?'

He nods.

The Emergency Duty Team is who foster carers call when something happens out of hours. He texts me:

The line was busy, so I left a message asking them to call back.

We reach the hospital in record time. No traffic on the roads. I realise I have no idea what the time is, but the large digits on my phone tell me it's nearly two o'clock in the morning. I'm still wired from dealing with the emergency. I expect the children are, too. And I'm left to wait while they stabilise Willow. Eventually I'm able to update Lloyd.

They're keeping her in. She's stable and sleeping now, after having her stomach pumped. Not much more I can do here for the time being. I'll get a taxi back from the hospital as soon as I can.

His text comes straight back: *Taxi? At this time of night? Better ask how much that will be first.*

True. Thoughts about cost go out of my head in a situation like this. In the taxi waiting area outside the hospital, I ask the question.

I'm quoted £90 'give or take'. It sounds like mostly 'take' to me. I don't need to do any calculation to know that would be almost half of our weekly allowance for Willow. There is no way that Rupert's department will reimburse that kind of sum without a fight.

I relay the information to Lloyd.

No way. I'll come and get you. The children are wide awake anyway.

I settle down to wait for him. I am utterly worn out. I am also sick of fighting. Fighting for every little penny when they waste so much money themselves. Money diverted to private companies who make massive profits by claiming that as private sector companies they can offer a better service. I'm sick of everything being a battle.

It's a lottery for any child caught in the system.

Chapter Thirty

Louise

In the morning, I'm up early, despite the fact that it was a ridiculously late night and I've barely slept. I email Rupert and Moira straight away, even though it's long before either would arrive at the office.

'Coffee?' Lloyd asks, when he comes down.

Yes, indeed. I need a big coffee, and fast. Today is going to be busy. I know that I will have to surrender any possibility of work to deal with social workers.

The children are all still in bed after all the drama, and there they will stay, although they should be at school. I quickly call the school and let them know that the children are too tired today 'after an incident last night with a foster child'. That probably won't cut it as a sound enough reason on the register. There probably isn't a code for that particular scenario. But it will also raise some red flags. No doubt there will be more follow-up calls and paperwork. There will probably be further wellness checks on the kids, which will take up more time; but we do live in a culture of litigation so a simple call is no longer enough, it seems. We call it 'due process' and tell ourselves that this is in the best interests of the child, but I rather suspect it's in the best interests of the organisation covering themselves.

We phone the hospital again first thing in the morning for an update and to find out about visiting hours. We are put through to the ward where a nurse explains that they won't be discharging her today; they're going to keep her in for at least another night.

Lloyd buys her a pair of rather expensive headphones en route, and takes in his old iPod, loaded with music she can listen to without needing to get online.

When we get there, it's still early. Willow is awake, but pale and washed out. And enormously apologetic for, 'All the mess I've caused.'

Poor child. All the pressure she has been under these last few days. Telling someone about her abusers should have been a release, should have helped her; instead it has been brutal.

I shake my head. Nothing to apologise for.

'I'm sorry, Louise. I didn't mean to make a fuss.'

'The hardest part is done, Willow. It will get easier now.'

She nods. I'm not sure she believes me. I don't know if I believe that myself.

I manage to get her password off her for her phone; she offers no resistance.

On the way back from the hospital I receive a call from Moira, who says that an emergency strategy meeting will take place, today, at ours, at midday. Which gives me just over an hour and a half to be ready. I hate it when they do this. And they do it continually: make the assumption that our homes and our lives are totally available for them at any hour of their choosing. I, of course, comply.

Back at home, with Lloyd and Lily, I go through Willow's phone. Lily is up and awake, which is useful because she knows where to look; Lloyd is there for moral support. Behind the calculator – which is not the calculator but an app to hide stuff in – a cache of horrendous suicide and cutting films are stored. It also transpires that she has been in regular communication with what I now know to be called a 'cut buddy'.

This 'buddy' has encouraged her to cut deeper and deeper, and to film it at the same time.

We shoo Lily off before it becomes too bleak.

As she's leaving, she calls out, 'Riley in year nine watched decapitation!'

I take a deep breath in. I seem to be doing a lot of that lately. I look at Lloyd and shake my head. His words echo my thoughts.

'What the fuck is this online world doing to children?'

I break rank once again and email Sally, our new favourite Child Protection Police Officer to let her know what we have found on Willow's phone and to update her with what's happened to Willow overnight.

I'm very tired. And when I feel like this, the raw injustices for the children bubble up to the surface and dominate all my thoughts and paths of action. Willow has been failed, so badly. She should never have had a bloody iPhone. If it had been left up to me, she wouldn't have. As the result of a flippant decision from someone not directly responsible for dealing with the day-to-day fallout, she was left even more vulnerable. All her unspoken pain and shame has led her to become drawn into the darkest areas of the human mind.

I shower quickly then dash to the shops, buy meal deals and treats and put them in each child's room with a note that a meeting is taking place in the kitchen. I'm conscious that I've neglected the poor dogs in all the drama. They haven't been for a walk yet. I check the clock, then scoot around with the hoover in record time, scan my emails and try to ignore all the work projects stuck to my studio wall that I am so behind on. An hour until the emergency strategy meeting.

I'm so tired and unfocused, it will do me good to take the dogs for a walk, get some fresh air and clear my head. By this late in the morning, the park is usually quiet. The pre-work dog walkers are at work, the school run is done and most of the retired have gone home and are finishing off their elevenses. I walk without thinking about anything other than Willow, and what might be said in the meeting. I pound along the lane to the big park area.

As I turn the corner I hear a woman's voice calling, 'Excuse me!'

I don't take much notice, but the voice gets louder and more school marmy. 'I say! Excuse meee! You, there.'

I stop and turn back around the corner. I have walked off without paying much attention to Dotty and Douglas, who know this walk like the back of their paws. I stand and look at this evidently disgruntled woman, genuinely confused about what on earth she might want with me.

'Yes?'

In what can best be described as a 'snotty' voice, she shouts out. 'You're disgusting! Your dogs have messed all up the path!'

I'm still confused. Both dogs went in the garden this morning and Doug did his second business at the beginning of the walk which I bagged and put in the dog poo bin. Whatever has happened, it won't have been my dogs. But Snotty School Marm is insistently waving her pointing finger, accusingly. 'People like you give dog walkers like me a bad name!'

She has a ginger Cockapoo on a lead. It looks timid and unhappy.

'I'm sorry, I didn't realise. I'm afraid I was a little preoccupied.'

She carries on berating me. Her Cockapoo looks on, almost apologetically. I decide it must be repressed.

I pull a poo bag out of my pocket and get it ready for scooping. The woman stands there, watching, as I walk along the path nearby, looking for all this mess. I can't see anything. She's still going, hammer and tongs.

'It would be helpful if you could tell me where my dog pooed?'

Instead of pointing specifically at the spot, she just stands there, waving her arm in the air screeching, 'Everywhere!'

I have had enough. I have no bandwidth left for anything else today. 'I think you are imagining it,' I say and walk off, assuming that will be the end of it.

But no, she paces behind me, telling me that she will call the police.

Jesus. I absolutely need to get away from this woman. She's doing my head in and I think she's actually bonkers. I quicken my pace.

She still follows, dragging her poor dog along by the lead. 'You should be more responsible. You need to watch out for your dogs. If you can't control them, then they shouldn't be off the lead! You need to have eyes on them at all times when they are out, so that you can see if they are going to the toilet,' she calls out, barely pausing for breath.

She evidently has hours of this material, but she's pushed my buttons too hard now. I just wanted a quiet walk to clear my head before the meeting. I turn around and say, 'Fuck off!'

Not my finest hour, admittedly, but it seems to do the trick. She turns on her heel and heads in the opposite direction. One of the friendly pensioners, John, who I have said hello to for years now, is coming the other way with his equally ancient-looking dog, Jasper. I look at him and sigh and shrug apologetically, assuming he has heard my rather blunt reaction.

He smiles, and puts his large, veiny old hand on my shoulder. 'Nutty as a fruit cake, that one.'

I smile back.

'Don't you worry. She'll have forgotten all about it by the time she gets home,' and winks before walking on.

By the time I get home I haven't forgotten. I am agitated.

Even more so because I spy Rupert's blue Fiat 500 over the road with two other people in it, and Moira in her car, parked a little further ahead, on the phone. At this stage in her demob-ship she's more likely ordering cupcakes for the office party on Friday than dealing with this situation, but I'm probably doing her a disservice. I'm in an ugly mood, and the walk hasn't calmed me down as it should have! But they're all early and I'm not ready. 'See you at 12!' I yell, with a casual wave. No one's stepping foot over my threshold a minute before.

And in comes a police car next, and parks right outside the house. Terrific!

We are already known in the area as 'The Fostering House'. People will be busy making their judgements. No doubt thinking how 'those naughty kids have been shoplifting again, or doing drugs'. They couldn't be further from the truth. What they really need to be thinking is, 'that poor child has been got at by online sickos who have tricked her into nearly cutting her foot off', and that's after months of systematic abuse. I'd like to scream it from the rooftops, but that wouldn't be fair on Willow.

I hang the leads up and call Lloyd, who has already got the kitchen table ready. 'The vultures are circling outside.' I know that they're here to help Willow, but it all feels vaguely threatening.

There will be seven of us. Lloyd has dragged in his yellow Pantone chair from his office. I'll give that to Rupert as he's young and funky, plus the chair is the least comfortable of all the odd chairs around the table, as far as I'm concerned. I haven't even had a chance to check in on Vincent, Lily and Jackson, who I assume are still in their rooms, probably sleeping. They really were all very tired – physically and emotionally.

When everyone is settled and Rupert is enthroned on the yellow Pantone chair, we begin with introductions. I learn who the other two people are in my kitchen. Kelly, I discover, is Rupert's new manager. I substitute 'new' for 'latest' in my head. I wonder how long she will last. The other is Craig. He is Kelly's manager. Quite the hierarchy.

In my experience, you only ever get this many social workers out when they are worried. Worried about a point of procedure, perhaps, as much as if not more than, a child. I suspect Craig's manager has briefed Craig not to make him or her look bad, or words to that effect. There is, understandably, an air of seriousness and solemnity to proceedings, although we can all talk with greater freedom than we might otherwise have done, since the subject under discussion is not present.

Sally announces that we will be joined by her Chief Inspector. Lots of 'rank' in this room. I look at Craig, who visibly bristles. There are various other eyes making contact across the room, and gestures between the members of the children's social care team. Lloyd gets up. 'In which case, I shall go and locate another chair.'

I can hear the thud of his footsteps walking about upstairs, where there is a spare antique dining chair in the dressing room. He comes back down carrying it. I imagine he will have chucked my pile of neatly folded scarves on the floor.

Aside from the huge human, emotional cost of what Willow has experienced, I am expecting today's meeting to be interesting. While the final introductions are taking place, the door goes and in comes Chief Inspector Decker. I hold back from saying it aloud, but on the inside I'm thinking, 'I've just seen your double.' I can see by Lloyd's face that he knows exactly what's going through my mind. Over time he has learnt the prompts for my terrible humour and bad puns.

Craig is just about to start the meeting when he is pipped at the post by Chief Inspector Decker, who efficiently lays out his understanding of why it has been necessary for us all to meet today.

'Since Louise contacted us, and with Willow's articulate descriptions and testimony, I am able to share with all of you that, as of last night, we have managed to make several arrests pertaining to this case.'

Wow. I wasn't expecting them to have moved so fast. That is a showstopping opening to proceedings. And it's a huge relief amidst all the horror.

'It's important to remember that this is a story of a vulnerable adult in the first instance, who was taken advantage of by a dangerous, organised and very sick group, who piggybacked off the church but were not religious in any way. Jason was groomed just as much as Willow, and both grew used to the 'prayer nights' that happened once a week, where Willow was subjected to the horrific sexual abuse that we now know about. It was sustained over several years. The group who infiltrated Willow and Jason's church had a number of homes that they visited, so as not to raise suspicion within the communities. But they always chose vulnerable adults in deprived areas and isolated them through their attendance at the church. The church itself was full of good, kind people who believed in God and the Christian faith and genuinely wanted to fulfil Christian ideals. The Moloc men, as we are calling them, were using the church for their own twisted ends. We believe that all the men who were responsible for sexually abusing Willow are now being held in custody.'

There is some further talk about that for a while and, as I listen, I wonder whether I've ever been in a meeting imbued with such weight and gravitas.

Apart from Rupert. Rupert sits in the yellow Pantone chair looking faintly ridiculous, with the expression of a rabbit caught in headlights.

Sally takes over and explains the next steps from the prosecution point of view. Then Craig asks Rupert to update us all about Willow.

Not only is this absolutely insulting, it's also stupid. We are the ones who have been dealing with it, and Rupert only knows what we have shared with him in brief email updates. I look around the table and wonder if it's only me who recognises the absurdity.

Rupert does *not* say, 'Perhaps Louise and Lloyd would be best placed to answer that question.' Instead, he clears his throat, and says, 'As far as we know, Willow's condition is stable.'

Perhaps sensing my inner rage, or simply being more emotionally in tune with what is happening here, Sally looks towards me. 'Louise, perhaps you can also update us on Willow's situation? I gather you've seen her at the hospital this morning?'

The meeting feels so serious that I'm a little intimidated. I don't feel comfortable about sharing too much. I choose my words carefully. 'Willow attempted an overdose last night. We found four empty packets of paracetamol in her bedside drawer. She cut her ankle so deeply that she had to go to hospital, where she currently remains. She has had more than 30 stitches in the cut.' Get me, all serious and grown-up.

We then talk about the phone. But here I am determined to make my point heard. 'We were never keen for Willow to have a phone, particularly an iPhone, since Willow had been kept away from social media until that point. Until we were told that she should have the phone.'

Craig is straight in, almost cutting me off before I've finished. 'Louise and Lloyd, why didn't you call EDT and follow protocols?'

And so, the blame game begins. As I knew it would.

Lloyd calmly pulls out his phone from his back pocket, scrolls to the recent calls list and turns the phone around to show the table. 'We did. I called them *twice*. Both times it rang several times and then went to their answerphone. I left my details twice, and no one got back to me. Oh and I did *clearly* state the seriousness of the situation. Louise and I are well aware of the protocols.'

Although she is not chairing, officially, Sally raises a questioning eyebrow in the direction of Craig and Kelly. Lloyd has returned their serve, and it's time to see if they'll hit one back over the net.

Kelly says, 'Oh, I think they were very busy that night.'

That night? It was last night. I can't help but feel that Kelly and her colleagues are sailing fairly close to the wind. Chief Inspector Decker and Sally brush over the intended snipe and we move on, but I'm sure it did not go unnoticed.

'Well, thanks to the prompt actions of Louise and Lloyd calling us and sending over some screenshots of conversations from Willow's phone to the team, we've been able to open a second investigation,' Sally informs us. 'The second investigation is looking into the abuse of girls who have been groomed by gangs to create extreme films of self-harming, that are then sold on hidden hubs.'

We all know that Willow has the phone because of Rupert – and whichever manager was there at the time – supporting his decision. He gave those sick people access to Willow. I suddenly start crying, and shake my head. Having promised myself that I'd only answer questions that are asked of me, I can't help but blurt out, 'What are we *doing* to children?'

Sally puts a reassuring hand on my arm. It's a sweet gesture and I'm grateful for it. She continues to talk. 'It doesn't need reiterating how serious the situation is. We are pulling in a team from another county who have come across the Moloc group before. Given the lack of online presence, so little is known about them, so we need to pool what we do know by working with colleagues across the country.'

I wonder why it isn't the social services representatives present who report on the next bit, but Sally continues. 'Adult social care services are now working with Jason, Willow's father, directly, to support him. His vulnerability here is not to be underestimated, and was very much the reason that the group targeted him and were able to gain access to Willow. But these developments also provide us with an opportunity: our team will work with adult social care to raise awareness about vulnerable adults with children who are targeted in the way that we've seen in this case. We have set up a meeting with Crimestoppers and invited churches and other organisations who work with vulnerable adults.'

I take a deep breath and sigh as I think about Susan and Adrian, who ditched Willow in her hour of need after she disclosed to them. I can only assume it was to protect their Christian standing in the community and with the church, and for Adrian to maintain his business reputation as the director of a fostering agency. It's as simple as that. I have a bitter taste in my mouth as I think about how they have put their own needs above hers, and made such a damaging accusation in the process. Willow needed love, help and support – not rejection.

And, just as I'm feeling that there is light at the end of the tunnel here, that some good can come out of all of this, Craig drops the bombshell.

Chapter Thirty-One

Louise

'Great work, Sally, thank you. We have also been busy this end,' Craig says. 'In light of last night's events–'

I want to throttle him. Last night might be 'events' to him, but it was an emotionally-charged emergency for our household, and it could have ended so much more tragically for Willow.

'–you'll be pleased to know that we have managed to find Willow a secure unit. It will be in her best interests to go there once she has been discharged from hospital.'

'As soon as we know when she is likely to be discharged, I'll be able to collect her and drive her straight there to settle her in,' Rupert adds.

What? In her *best* interests? Are they serious? Are these people out of their minds? What are they thinking? Why the hell have they made this monstrous decision? Willow needs to be here, with us.

My heart sinks once more.

But I know why they have done it. It's because Willow's emergency happened on our watch. Sally once again reaches out and puts a comforting hand on my arm. Even though this is our kitchen, in our home, I can't say what I really want to.

Lloyd asks, 'Where is the unit and when can we visit her?'

Kelly says, 'Unfortunately, given the waiting lists for this kind of care, we could not find one in the region, but we have managed to find one in another county.'

The police sharing information across counties to track down sex abusers is one thing. But moving a child out of county? Away from everything she knows?

'Where?' I can barely speak.

The tension in the room is palpable. No one comments for a moment, perhaps all waiting for someone else to speak.

'Leeds,' Craig says, eventually.

My eyes are probably like saucers. 'What?'

Leeds isn't just across the border into the next county, it's the other side of the country! That means uprooting her from school as well as us.

Rupert ignores me and says, 'So, if you could pack up Willow's stuff, Louise, I will collect it from you tomorrow.'

This is madness. I know it, and at least half of the people around this table know it. And the other half should know better. I can't tell them how ridiculous this decision is, so instead I ask Rupert how he's going to fit all her possessions into his car.

Kelly responds. 'Don't worry, Louise, we've thought about that. We are hiring a large estate to take Willow's stuff in. Rupert will be here to collect her things tomorrow at—' she looks down at her notebook. 'At 2pm.'

It is a done deal.

But it can't be. That can't be it. I say, 'I want to say goodbye. We all want to say goodbye. The children will want to say goodbye. My son, who called the ambulance. My other son, who soothed Willow until the paramedics arrived. Lily, who helped find the evidence on her phone. They will all want to say goodbye.'

There is another awkward pause. The three on the social services team look at each other in a way that reveals that they had not thought about this. Chief Inspector Decker stares at them incredulously. If I didn't know better, I'd say he looks like he's going to punch them. Moira, who has said absolutely nothing, looks at Craig.

He runs his finger in the space between his collar and his neck, as though it is a little too tight for him.

'Yes,' he says, eventually. 'You can say goodbye.'

Epilogue

In the end, Willow was kept in hospital for three nights. Rupert collected her things the next day, and we continued to visit her each of the days in hospital. Our goodbyes were said standing round her hospital bed.

I miss Willow.

We all do. The household is changed without her gentle presence, her kindness, her music and her quirky humour. We all loved her, and still do. We will never get over how her placement ended so abruptly. It was shocking and we were heartbroken.

Moira left shortly afterwards and moved on to her new life in wedding planning and events. I wish her well. I'm sure it will have its stressful moments, but nothing like the stress that social workers are under, constantly.

I gave her a card and a bunch of flowers from the independent florist just outside town. A small token, but I hope that she would have appreciated my effort. We have had our moments where we have disagreed, but overall we have worked well together and I know she has a good heart. If I think about it, I could probably pinpoint the exact moment when she began to step back from the role emotionally. Knowing what I do, I fully understand that social workers need to look after their own mental health, too.

But so do foster carers. We are still being treated like robots. We are spoken to as if we do not have feelings. What happened with Willow crushed me. We had, naturally, grown close to her over the time she spent in our household. Because of her disclosure to me, because of my past, because of what she'd been through, I felt that I understood some of her pain. We had a connection, and I wanted what was best for her. I still maintain, if anyone would listen, that taking her away from us so brutally was unforgivable; for her, even more than for us.

Not all of the children who stay with us find a happy ending. Many of the children I have chosen to write about in Thrown Away Children do. Readers want to hear about the success stories. Sadly, what happened to Willow, after she left here so swiftly, was, perhaps predictably, not good. Not good at all. Although it took me a little bit of time to find that out.

I was not allowed to see Willow for a long time after she was discharged from the hospital. Too long. I kept emailing and calling Rupert, but I got no response. After a few months, Rupert was promoted to a management position, so his career was on an upwards trajectory, in spite of all the shortcomings we saw in the way he acted. I feel a kind of despair just knowing that.

Eventually, I found out where Willow had gone through other contacts. Willow had been placed in an unregulated 'wellbeing centre'. Ruthlessly, some might say, I approached this particular residential home, who had been looking after her for six months by the time I tracked it down. The staff agreed to meet with me after I kept asking and wouldn't take no for an answer. Under my repeated requests, it was agreed that they would talk to Willow's latest social worker about the possibility of me being able to meet with her.

After several more weeks, still not being able to contact her directly, not even being able to send her a letter, I was finally allowed to see her. The moment we saw each other, in the sitting room of her residential home, we ran to each other and hugged. Through her clothing I could feel how thin and frail she had become. I suspected an eating disorder was beginning to creep in as well as everything else. She was simply broken by all the abuse, and her trauma was compounded by the feelings of rejection.

I just wanted to pick her up and take her home and care for her and keep her safe. Of course that was never going to be allowed.

It transpired that she had been prescribed Fluoxetine. Her mood deteriorated. While she was in the unregulated home, which, incidentally, was costing the local authority something in the region of £15,000 per week, she was supposedly under constant surveillance. Given her history, that meant that Willow was checked on every 15 minutes of the day and night, even when she was in the shower or on the loo. Most of the staff at the centre were male. A small number of the duty nurses were female. This wasn't a good ratio for Willow, who was, understandably, uncomfortable around men.

The combination of essentially being under the gaze of all these men (however professional the intention) 'watching' her 24-7, plus the Fluoxetine, made her worse. I suspect that being away from us, a home where she had flourished for a while, also contributed to that decline, especially given the way she greeted me.

The quarter of an hour checking rule meant that even if Willow wanted to go outside into the garden they had to complete a risk assessment form and a member of staff had to be near her. I devoted much time and energy into convincing Willow's new social worker and their new manager that I would be more than happy to provide Willow with respite at the weekends, for her to have a break from the institutional setting.

She did come for a single night. I picked her up from the residential home to drive her back to ours. While I waited I became aware of other girls in the home, walking around looking as desperately sad as Willow. It was utterly terrifying to know that Willow's story was being repeated. That other young girls were going through what she was.

I had to complete enormous amounts of paperwork to enable the visit to happen. It was paperwork which essentially relieved the home of any responsibility should anything happen. The wording seemed to be designed with litigation in mind, rather than the wellbeing of Willow.

It reinforced my belief that children's social care services are actually dominated by insurance requirements, not sensible caring policies.

The drive back to our house took more than three hours, and although it was tiring for Willow, I enjoyed every second of it. I played all her favourite music, remembering all the tracks that she had loved to listen to while she was living with us.

She spent so much time looking out of the window. It was hard not to notice the way she sat with her hands on her lap, circling her thumbs around and around. I chatted about home and tried not to ask too many questions.

Once home the others came to say hello. Everyone was gentle because we could all see that she was fragile. Not so for Dotty and Douglas! They were not having any of that, thank you very much. Both bounded up to her, evidently delighted to be reunited. Mabel, Lily's cat, also came in for some attention.

I love this about animals: the way they can always cut through our rubbish. The furry ones helped to break the ice a little, and make Willow's temporary return feel a little bit more 'normal'.

As the afternoon went on, Willow drifted about, but seemed happiest sitting on the floor with the dogs. She didn't talk much, but did mention things about the home, and some of the girls in residence by name.

'Oh, you've made some friends?'

'No.'

I raised a quizzical eyebrow, but she left it at that.

I had made all her favourite food and filled the cupboards and fridge with every possible snack that she might like. The others were on strict command not to eat everything. I had organised a movie night so that it felt spontaneous, like old times. I did not want to put her under any pressure. She sat on the sofa next to me, with her head on my shoulder, and I gently stroked her hair. The others were sprawled out on cushions and sofas. Lloyd was on refreshments and snacks duty.

She went to bed in her old room. By this point we had had a couple of short term placements in there since her abrupt departure, but I had kept the layout the same and anything that hadn't gone with her that I had kept hold of was displayed in her room. I hoped it would create an association of safety, and memories of feeling safe and calm.

As directed, I gave her the prescribed medications before she went to bed. The house had been thoroughly checked to make sure that there were no other medicines that she could access, nor sharp objects or blades. I had my own memories of that last night to keep me on the alert, and I went into her room several times once she was settled before I finally convinced myself that all would be well and went to bed myself.

In the morning she definitely seemed more relaxed. Jackson, Vincent and Lily had already decided that the plan for the day involved McDonald's at lunchtime, via the beach for a run around.

Sitting on the big flat rocks at the pebbly beach, looking far out to sea, Willow opened up a little more.

'What are they like? The other girls at the home?'

'Horrible.'

I probed a little more. After a sigh, Willow pulled out her phone and played me a recording of what I can only describe as a violent, bullying, bitch-fest.

'That was last week.'

It made my heart ache and I felt a rising sense of panic when I heard the way a member of staff intervened in the exchange. I say 'intervened', but actually all they said was, 'that's not very kind,' and did absolutely nothing about the torrent of abuse that was being hurled in Willow's direction.

For a flavour, they were calling Willow a 'fucking dyke' and 'a freak' who was only 'attention-seeking'. She was a 'crazy bitch' and much worse.

'Can you send me those? Ping them over?'

Willow shook her head.

'No. If you say anything, it will be even worse. You can't do anything about it.'

'Oh, Willow.'

'It's not just me, anyway.'

Willow told me that there were other recordings of girls attacking other girls verbally and physically.

'And where are the staff when all this is going on?' I ask.

'It doesn't matter whether they're around or not. They don't do anything.'

I could well believe it.

All of which made me feel as if I didn't want to take Willow back there. I knew I had to, of course. And in case I needed reminding, texts and emails kept arriving from the home to confirm our time of return.

I made sure that I got Willow back to the home on time, but watched her shoulders slope and her heart sink as we reached the front door. I stood by the door for as long as we dared, stroking her hair.

'Call me if you need me.'

The member of staff put her arm around Willow to direct her back into the house. As I walked towards the car I turned around and looked up at the windows. Prying eyes of girls with sour faces. Girls who had been through Lord only knows what. Girls who only knew how to survive through abusing others.

Willow did not reply to my texts and, after a few days, I called the home again. I learnt that Willow had taken an overdose and cut herself extremely deeply on the wrists. She was in hospital and would not be returning to the home. Instead she was going to be moved to a secure psychiatric unit.

'She took those actions on the evening she returned from her visit with you. Perhaps it would be for the best if you didn't attempt to contact her again.'

The blame was being well and truly laid at my door. We received official communications in writing a few days later. The powers that be had decided that Willow could not have further contact with me or our family since it was 'too traumatic' and 'triggered her suicide attempt'.

I remain, to this day, heartbroken.

I don't know what the final outcome for Willow will be. Of course, I glean what I can on the foster carers' wires. Willow's cutting continues to be a problem, in spite of the surveillance. The 'secure' unit is, to the best of my knowledge, at least more regulated than the home was, and what is described as 'purpose-built'. The walls slope so that children can't hang themselves. The rest of it looks like a prison cell. It isn't a place to inspire any kind of joy of living.

As far as I know, Willow has stopped listening to, and playing, her music.

Afterword

Willow is the first story I have shared where there is no happy ending.

Yet.

As I write this, her life is, to all intents and purposes, suspended – while she navigates a system that is more or less designed to see her fail, when it should be protecting her and helping her to survive. I honestly feel that relating Willow's experience is akin to watching people punching a kitten.

The terrible, incomprehensible sexual abuses she suffered were on top of the challenges of being brought up by a father with such severe learning needs.

If the right help had been forthcoming for Jason sooner, then Willow might have been saved. Since our experience with Willow I have met other children whose parents had learning issues and were tricked into letting their children be used for sex or other exploitation.

I have a friend who looked after a young girl with a baby, whose mother had learning issues. This friend took them both in: Melissa, and her little baby boy. No one knew who the father was. As time went on and my friend, a brilliant foster carer, got to know Melissa better, she pieced the jigsaw together and learnt that the girl had been systematically abused. Men in the area preyed on Melissa's mother to get access to her daughter, just like Willow's case. Melissa would sit in her room waiting for different men to have sex with her, whilst her mum genuinely believed everything was fine and that was her normal.

The daughter was repeatedly abused by these men, and became pregnant. Parents with learning issues, especially ones who are on their own, can also be preyed upon by predators who want access to their homes for cuckooing. Cuckooing is when organised crime groups, gangs or drug dealers target vulnerable people and use their homes, usually to deal drugs from. I think that Jason was an easy target for cuckooing several times in his life. But worse still is when those vulnerable adults are targeted for access to their children. We live in a dark world.

The other theme that emerged in the telling of Willow's story, not for the first time in the *Thrown Away Children* series it has to be said, is the problem of mobile phones, and what their use might unwittingly unleash into our homes. Parents need to arm themselves against this unseen enemy. Take a look, for example, at *App Hider* on your phone app browser for the kind of hidden apps that children might install on their mobile phones.

But I think another layer to Willow's story which makes it so tragic is the fact that the system also failed to protect Willow from Adrian and Susan who, in spite of their holier-than-thou image, were complicit in the abuse by keeping quiet about it. They threw Willow under the bus by making a wild allegation about her in order to save their reputations. Adrian ran an independent foster agency, for goodness' sake.

While writing *Willow's Story*, our lives became much busier. I mentioned it early on, but I was in the final stages of setting up Spark Sisterhood, my charity for girls in and leaving care. I was also signed by Mirror Books for S*lave Girls*, a brand new series of true life stories.

Meanwhile, I'm delighted to be with a new fostering agency, Fostering UK, a family-run outfit. I'm delighted that we've made the switch. Other independent fostering services have put barriers in the way. I know it's because I have a bit of a reputation for saying it as it is, and caring about the children more than the paperwork. I make no apology for that. But our experiences so far reassure me that there are still ways of doing right by the children who end up – through no fault of their own – in care. When Nelson Mandela launched the Children's Fund in South Africa in May 1995, he gave a speech which famously included the words: 'There can be no keener revelation of a society's soul than the way in which it treats its children.'

We have a long way to go to cleanse our society's soul if the current state of the care system is anything to go by.

Acknowledgements

I am eternally grateful to the constant few people in my life without whom these stories would never see the light of day.

Firstly to Lloyd, who, like me, is doubly sad right now, both at Lily's departure and at Willow's situation. To Jackson and Vincent, who were both shocked by the abrupt way that Willow's placement ended, but have also had to deal with saying goodbye to someone they had come to think of as their sister.

To Theresa Gooda, who is always on the other end of the phone or text, sending comfort and wisdom.

I am lucky to have a collective of readers: Catherine Lloyd, Alexandra Plowman and Karen Furse, who always read the first draft of the manuscript. They have been with me from the very beginning of the *Thrown Away Children* journey, and I am so grateful.

To Jane Graham Maw, my very special agent who always has my back; and Jo Sollis, the most wonderful editor you could ask for. Also to Claire Brown, who sorts out my PR.

Finally, I've mentioned them throughout this narrative

and above in the Afterword, but I would like to acknowledge and thank Fostering UK, a small family run fostering agency, for welcoming me and my family, and bending over backwards to support our foster children.

Help and Information

I am the founder of Spark Sisterhood

The traditional goodbye-and-good-luck approach for girls leaving care is outdated. It leaves girls vulnerable to cycles of struggle and adversity, incl. social exclusion, homelessness, unemployment, drug abuse and other challenges. We're here to change that narrative. With our employment pathways, mentoring program, community and online learning platform, we're reshaping post-care experiences for girls across the UK.

Website: https://www.sparksisterhood.org

Email: louise@louise-allen.com

My essential 'must-haves' to support with foster care:

FosterWiki is designed to help empower Foster Carers with knowledge, through examples and experiences of other Foster Carers.

Website: https://fosterwiki.com/

Email: info@fosterwiki.com

I now foster with Fostering UK. A growing number of foster agencies are owned by private equity companies with the sole aim of making money. This has never been the intention of Fostering UK, and never will be.

Website: https://fosteringuk.org.uk/
Phone: 0333 044 8890

Finally, the National Union of Professional Foster Carers (NUPFC) provides valuable assistance and services to its members, including representation during the allegations process, representation during standard of care proceedings, as well as helping to find solutions to problems that may occur between you and your foster agency or local authority.

Website: https://nupfc.com/
Phone: 0800 915 1570
Email: enquiries@nupfc.com

COMING SOON

A BRAND NEW LOUISE ALLEN SERIES

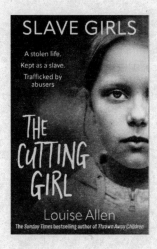

SLAVE GIRLS

Louise Allen

with Theresa McEvoy

Charlotte - The Cutting Girl - comes from a family of high achievers. Her father is a politician, and her mother is a senior medical officer.

When she moves from her prestigious boarding school she is groomed by a girl two years her senior, spiralling into a cycle of drugs, self-harm and sexual abuse.

When she goes missing, five other girls do, too. A nationwide media campaign sets out to track them down, but can Charlotte ever escape the gang behind the abduction and abuse?

THROWN AWAY **CHILDREN:**
COMING SOON TO THE SERIES

MILO'S STORY
Louise Allen
with Theresa McEvoy

Michelle and Andy are thrilled to be fast-tracked into fostering and are quickly paired with 7-year-old Milo

But Milo tears through their home like a raging tornado, destroying a beautiful interior – and their lives.

What are the secrets of his violent and destructive behaviours? Experienced foster carer Louise Allen steps in. Can she uncover the little boy's disturbing past and help him?

THROWN AWAY **CHILDREN**: OTHER BOOKS IN THIS SERIES

MARILYN'S STORY
Louise Allen
with Theresa McEvoy

An unhealthy obsession and a dark secret spell trouble in a disturbing case for the Allen household

A baby is named 'Marilyn' after the Hollywood legend, Norma Jean. Marilyn inherits her parents' fascination for Marilyn Monroe and develops an obsession with her alter-ego.

When her family is torn apart by tragedy, she finds herself in the care system, and systematically derails foster-carer Louise's family holiday. But is her diva behaviour masking a dark secret?

THROWN AWAY **CHILDREN:**
OTHER BOOKS IN THIS SERIES

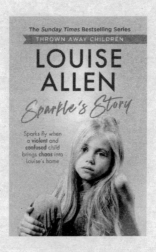

SPARKLE'S STORY
Louise Allen
with Theresa McEvoy

Louise gets a frantic call to take in a damaged and destructive young girl. Separated from her siblings Sparkle is hostile and angry.

A short while after settling in Sparkle begins to identify as pansexual. A revolution is underway in the Allen household, with Sparkle's transition motivating all of the young people to explore what becoming an adult means for them and the language and communication between everyone is in uproar.

But it's Sparkle's escalating behaviour that causes concern.

THROWN AWAY CHILDREN:
OTHER BOOKS IN THIS SERIES

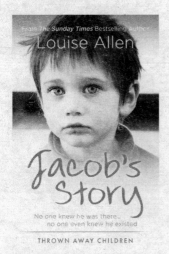

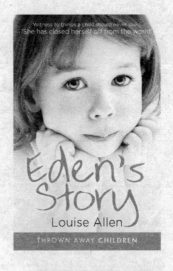

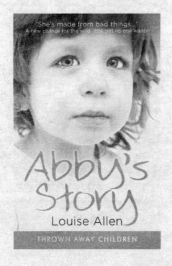